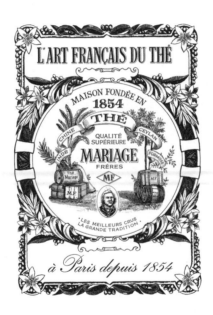

'The fragrance of adventure and poetry endlessly pervades each cup of tea'

Henri Mariage,
Founder, MARIAGE FRÈRES.

MARIAGE FRÈRES : THE FRENCH ART OF TEA

For several generations now, MARIAGE FRÈRES' passion for tea has been governed by an aesthetic sense of refinement and a quest for perfection.
It was back in the seventeenth century that the ancestors of the MARIAGE family established the principles that subsequently developed into a veritable

French Art of Tea

French connoisseurs, led by MARIAGE FRÈRES, are sensitive to everything surrounding the 'spiritual beverage', and skilfully combine considerations of taste and aesthetic appearance with cultural traditions

The Finest Harvests

Fine pluckings from the most prestigious estates on earth are avidly sought for that delicate bouquet which epitomizes French taste.

A Grand Tradition of Blends

Like the alchemy behind fine perfumes, the sophisticated blending of sublime teas constantly enriches the range of tastes offered to connoisseurs

The Art of Tea Tasting

French expertise highlights the right preparation method for a given tea, the quality of the water, control of temperature, correct steeping time, and careful selection of just the right teapot.

Tea and Gastronomy

Elaborated according to age-old tradition, gastronomic guidelines permit tea's noble flavour to accompany culinary dishes, pastries, and sweets. A delight for gourmet palates.

The Design and Reproduction of Tea Equipage

In a spirit of elegance and simplicity, modern and traditional tea equipage evokes distant voyages and legends from the world of tea.

The Art of Serving Tea

French savoir-faire based on a tradition of elegance, refined settings, and an innate sense of festivity has developed into the fine art of receiving guests for tea.

Thé Français - 'French Tea' is a rich blend of cultural traditions, as epitomised by MARIAGE FRÈRES. It now constitutes

The French School of Tea

THE SPIRIT OF TEA

'Tea: a gift from heaven,
a spiritual beverage
for humanity'

'Tea must be deserved; it is demanding.
Every harvest has its own nature, its secrets'

'Tea is a noble beverage.
Preparing it is an art that combines
skill and tradition'

'Tea weds an individual's consciousness;
it is the surest marker of the soul'

'Tea stirs poetic feeling
and inspires gentle reverie'

Henri Mariage,
Founder, MARIAGE FRÈRES

MARIAGE FRÈRES : THE FRENCH TEA HOUSE

On the origin of the MARIAGE *family and the key role it played in the colonial tea and spice trade in France.*

*A*ROUND 1660, NICOLAS MARIAGE MADE SEVERAL VOYAGES TO PERSIA, THE East Indies, and the Moghul Empire. He was part of a deputation dispatched by King Louis XIV and the French East India Company to sign a trade agreement with the Shah of Persia.

Meanwhile, Nicolas's brother, Pierre MARIAGE, travelled to the island of Madagascar on behalf of the same company.

A century later, Jean-François MARIAGE, born in 1766, was still trading in tea, spices, and other colonial goods in Lille, where he taught the business to his four sons–Louis, Aimé, Charles, and Auguste. Around 1820, Louis, Aimé, and Charles jointly took over the firm from their father, while in 1845 Aimé and Auguste, already living on Rue Bourg-Tibourg in Paris, together founded 'AUGUSTE MARIAGE & COMPAGNIE', thereby perpetuating the family tradition.

LA ROUTE DU THÉ
DE LA SAISON 1854-1855
Shanghaï · Foochow · Amoy · Hong Kong
Whampoa · Canton · Macao · Le Havre

Aimé's sons, Henri and Edouard MARIAGE, in turn learned the family trade at their father's side, and finally founded the MARIAGE FRÈRES tea company in Paris on June 1, 1854. They did business with the most distant trading posts in China and Ceylon. As the oldest French importer of tea, MARIAGE FRÈRES supplied the most exclusive retailers, delicatessens, tea rooms, and hotels. The excellence of its products and its great respect for the French art of tea have always been recognized and appreciated.

After 130 years of existence, MARIAGE FRÈRES decided to enter the retail business, selling more than 500 high quality teas over the counter and by mail-order. In addition to supplying tea grown in 35 different countries, MARIAGE FRÈRES perpetuates the fine art of serving tea through the design and reproduction of exclusive teapots, tea services, and other utensils.

The MARIAGE FRÈRES company is still located in the historic Marais district of Paris, and the building has remained intact. Old China tea chests, scales, sieves, and colonial countertops are still used, making the shop a veritable museum. On entering the store, visitors are struck by the fragrance of tea that has impregnated the walls and woodwork over the years. These same walls also house a tea room in a colonial decor that harmoniously and charmingly combines marble, Venetian-style paintings, natural rattan, and exotic plants beneath a glass ceiling. Customers brunch or lunch on highly refined dishes made with tea, or simply enjoy pastries, ice cream, jellies or home-made cocktails–all, of course, made with tea. Tea time can be a very special moment, indeed.

MARIAGE FRÈRES boasts two other Paris branches. In December 1990, a second boutique opened on the Left Bank of Paris; housed in an authentic seventeenth-century building, the shop evokes the spirit of the French East India Company. Then in December 1997, a third branch opened in a prestigious nineteenth-century building in the Monceau district of the Right Bank, representing the cultural blend of the days of France's famous Colonial Exposition. Furthermore, each MARIAGE FRÈRES outlet features a unique tea museum. Finally, in November 1999, at 35 Rue du Bourg-Tibourg, MARIAGE FRÈRES inaugurated its 'THÉ FRANÇAIS' tea counter, a showcase for immediate delectation of this rich tradition of flavours - the finest harvests and flavoured blends are pre-packaged for easy purchase, along with gourmet treats made from tea.

Desirous of making the French Art of Tea known to the world, MARIAGE FRÈRES also moved to Japan. In the historic Ginza district and in the trendy Shinjuku area of Tokyo, as well as in famous neighbourhoods in Kyoto, Kobe, and Osaka, its *Maisons de Thé* encourage the heirs of *cha no yu* to enjoy a harmonious blend of traditions.

In order to share its experience more widely, MARIAGE FRÈRES has undertaken to publish this book, which explains the art of selecting the right tea for the right moment. A sublime moment of delectation that triggers sensations of the distant garden where the tea was plucked–a truly grand voyage.

The true Home of Tea, where every detail is authentic.

Welcome to the World of fine Tea !

THE CIVILIZATION OF TEA

' *Tea was not only a remedy against drowsiness. It was a way of aiding men to return to their sources, a moment in the rythm of the day when prince and peasant shared the same thoughts and same happiness while preparing to return to their respective fates.'*

Lu Yu (733–804)
Cha King ('The Holy Scripture of Tea')
The first book devoted to tea

THE ADVENTURE OF TEA

LEGENDS OF THE SPIRITUAL BEVERAGE

The subject of several charming legends, tea has the privilege of being the most ancient beverage in the world. It is nearly 5,000 years old, and its true origins remain shrouded in mystery.

CCORDING TO CHINESE LEGEND, Emperor Chen-Nung, known as the 'Divine Harvester', was very strict about hygiene and drank only boiled water. One day in the year 2737 BC., as the emperor was sitting at rest under a wild tea tree gently blowing in the breeze, a few leaves tumbled into his cup. On drinking it, the emperor was filled with inexpressible well-being. Tea was born.

INDIANS, MEANWHILE, ATTRIBUTE THE discovery of tea to Prince Bhodi-Dharma, son of Kosjuwo, king of the Indies. The venerable prince travelled from southern India to China during the reign of Emperor Xuanwudi, preaching Buddhism in the kingdom of North Wei. He advocated meditation, the cultivation of the mind, and the elimination of all illusion as the path to salvation. The prince also made the vow to meditate for seven years without ever falling asleep. At the end of five years, he was overcome with weariness and sleep, but a providential act made him gather and chew a few leaves from an unknown tree.

It was of course a tea tree, and the amazing virtues of tea gave the prince the strength to fulfil his vow.

JAPANESE LEGEND TELLS A SOMEWHAT different version of this same story. After only three years of meditation, Prince Bhodi-Dharma fell asleep and dreamed of the women he had once loved.

On waking, furious at his weakness, he tore off his eyelids and buried them. Returning to the same spot some time later, he noticed that the eyelids had sprouted into an unknown bush. On chewing the leaves, he realized that they had the effect of keeping his eyes open.

He recounted the story to his friends, who gathered the seeds and thus began planting tea.

It is said that the prince fled China for Japan, taking tea with him.

Prince Bhodi-Dharma's journey to China is mentioned in Chinese chronicles dating from the reign of Vu Yu, in 543 AD.

THE TEA ROUTE

*B*Y THE FOURTH CENTURY, tea was being consumed extensively in China.

The preparation of tea evolved through three historical stages: boiled tea, whipped tea, and steeped tea.

These three 'schools of tea' reflect the spirit of the period during which each one predominated, for they correspond to China's Tang, Song, and Ming dynasties.

In the eighth century, tea became a royal drink, and the nobility adopted it as an elegant pastime. Poet Lu Yu (733–804), at the height of the Tang dynasty, wrote the Cha King, or 'Holy Scripture of Tea', the first book ever written about tea.

Tea has played a key role in China's history. During the Song dynasty (960–1279), it was used as a measure of wealth throughout the empire, and was the object of a veritable state monopoly. Pressed into bricks, it served as currency.

The story of tea is also intimately bound up with world history. As it spread across the globe, tea tended to bring together people of widely differing religions and philosophies. Tea arrived in Japan in the ninth century, introduced by a Buddhist monk named Saicho. As far as the Japanese are concerned, tea is more than just a beverage. The object of the tea ceremony, which has fortunately survived the centuries and now transcends national borders, is to help the mind attain serenity.

Thanks to caravan trade routes, tea spread throughout the Mongol empire, Persia, the Islamic world, and Russia, before Europe learned of its existence. Long cut off from the East, Europe was late in discovering tea.

An Arab trader named Suleyman reportedly introduced it. Marco Polo, meanwhile, recounted in his famous Travels that a Chinese finance minister lost his post in 1285 for having arbitrarily raised the tax on tea.

Yet it was only in 1610 that tea truly began its remarkable expansion into the Western world.

The various East India Companies, which engaged in regular trade with the Far East, introduced tea into Holland in 1610, into France in 1636, and into England in 1650.

Tea also played a historic role in the American colonies, thanks to the notorious 'Boston Tea Party' on December 16, 1773, which triggered the American revolution.

It was not until the nineteenth century that tea became the national drink of England. It was allegedly Queen Victoria herself who started the habit of drinking tea at five o'clock. China was still practically the sole supplier of tea as late as the early nineteenth century. It was only in 1834 that tea plantations were introduced into India, spreading shortly afterward to Ceylon (1857), and then onto other countries of Asia, Africa, and South America.

Competition between shippers to arrive first with the new harvest at European ports led to races on the Far East maritime route, resulting in the building of the famous 'Tea Clippers' or 'China Clippers'.

In the 21ˢᵗ century, tea became the most widely consumed beverage in the world-at least one trillion cups are now drunk every year.

FRANCE DISCOVERS TEA

IN FRANCE, TEA SWIFTLY BECAME extremely popular.

One of the first French tea connoisseurs was Louis XIV. It is reported that in 1665 his doctors prescribed tea 'to aid digestion'. The king, having also been told that neither the Chinese nor Japanese suffered from gout or cardiac disorders, drank tea regularly for his health.

Later, on September 1, 1686, the Sun King—as Louis XIV was called—reportedly received a gold teacup from the famous Kosa Pan, ambassador for King Somdet Phra Narai of Siam. This magnificent gift was designed to spread the fame of the legendary brew.

The royal beverage soon became the

'Traités nouveaux et curieux du café, du thé et du chocolat' Monsieur Philippe Sylvestre Dufour, Lyon, 1685.
First book in French devoted to tea.

preferred drink of gentlemen who frequented court circles and aristocratic salons.
The divine plant, however, was not to the taste of certain ladies who favoured chocolate.

Tea's fervent supporters nevertheless included royal ministers like Chancellor Séguier and Cardinal Mazarin, the playwright Racine, and Madame de Genlis, the writer.

According to Madame de Sévigné's correspondence, the habit of adding milk to tea originated in France. It was the marquise de la Sablière who launched the idea, now imitated throughout the world.

Antoine Furetière, who compiled the first comprehensive dictionary of the French language (1684), devoted an entire page to tea. He noted that 'persons of the highest rank delight in preparing it themselves in their magnificent apartments, where they keep several precious vessels for that purpose'.

The introduction of tea nevertheless led to numerous controversies in medical circles.

In 1634, the Jesuit priest Alexander of Rhodes, who had spent thirty-five years in China, reported that tea cured his migraine headaches.

In 1648, a Monsieur Morisset defended a thesis before the faculty of medicine at the University of Paris, arguing that tea was 'mentally stimulating', to the distaste of ardent defenders of sage, who had Morisset's thesis burned!

Several other authors of learned treatises attempted to link tea to other known medicinal plants such as myrtle, fennel, and wild rose.

It was thanks to another doctor, François Souquet, that the taste for tea ultimately triumphed, to be finally adopted by the bourgeoisie in France around 1840.

'Drink French Tea!'

That was the slogan employed by Indochina's Union of Tea Planters when pitching their tea to French tea-drinkers in the early twentieth century. The French colonial government had made considerable efforts to promote tea grown on the high plateaux of Moïs in Indochina.

Attempts were also made to grow tea on Reunion Island off the coast of Africa, but without much success.

The French now drink 210 grams of tea per person per year, or about 100 cups.

A tea tree growing in the Botanical Gardens in Paris in 1782 was considered a rare and strange plant. In 1988, MARIAGE FRÈRES endowed those same gardens with a tea bush originally from the Japanese province of Shizuoka.

TEA AND THE ART OF FINE LIVING

In the East, tea is part of the art of fine living. The importance conferred on tea in Imperial China made it an indispensable part of every ceremony. During a wedding, for example, it symbolized long life and marital fidelity, since tea bushes live for a hundred years or more.

TEA AND GASTRONOMY

*T*EA IS A UNIVERSAL BEVERAGE, and accords favourably with French cuisine, easily accompanying both sweet and savory dishes. The opportunities for enjoying tea throughout the day are thereby multiplied.

Paris salon, circa 1900.

• *French breakfast*

Types of tea:
– China: Yunnan.
– India: Darjeeling, Assam, Terai, Dooars, Travancore, Nilgiri, Arunachal Pradesh.
– Ceylon: B.O.P., B.O.P.F., Pekoe, F.P.
– Indonesia.
– South America.
– Africa.
– Oceania.
– MARIAGE FRÈRES morning blends (non-smoky): Breakfast Earl Grey, Sultane, Gouverneur, De Londres, etc.

• English Breakfast

Types of tea:

- Smoky China: Lapsang Souchong, Tarry Souchong.
- India: Assam.
- Ceylon: B.O.P., B.O.P.F., Pekoe, F.P.
- Africa.
- Green teas from every region.
- MARIAGE FRÈRES smoky morning blends: Empereur Chen-Nung, Majesty, etc.

• Brunch

Types of tea:

- China: Yunnan.
- Smoky China: Lapsang Souchong.
- India: Darjeeling, Assam, Arunachal Pradesh.
- Ceylon: F.P., O.P., F.O.P.
- Green teas from every region.
- Blue teas from every region.
- MARIAGE FRÈRES morning blends.
- MARIAGE FRÈRES daytime blends.

• Lunch – Dinner

Fish, Seafood, Caviar

Types of tea:

- Green teas from every region.
- Blue teas from every region.
- Smoky teas.
- Earl Grey teas.

- MARIAGE FRÈRES mild smoky blends: Genghis Khan, Amateur, Cha King, Zodiac, etc.

Poultry

Types of tea:

- Smoky China.
- India: Darjeeling.
- Blue teas.
- Jasmine teas.

Spicy dishes

Types of tea:

- China: Keemun, Szechwan, Ching-Wo.
- India: Darjeeling, Arunachal Pradesh.
- Ceylon: F.P., O.P.
- Green teas: Lotus d'Or, Sencha, etc.
- Blue teas.
- Jasmine teas.

• After meals

Types of tea:

- China: Keemun, Szechwan, Ching-Wo.
- Inde : Darjeeling.
- Green teas : Lotus d'or, Sencha, etc.
- Blue teas.
- Matured teas.
- MARIAGE FRÈRES evening blends.

• Tea Breaks or Tea Time

Types of tea:

- All types.
- MARIAGE FRÈRES blends for daytime or evening.
- Flavoured teas.
- Flavoured blends.

MENU

SABLÉS AU THÉ

CHOCOLAT DES MANDARINS

BONBONS AU THÉ MARIAGE FRÈRES

• Using Tea as a Cooking Ingredient

Tea has always played a special role in the preparation of refined oriental dishes.

Its subtle flavour also harmonizes well with French and international cuisine, delicately enhancing both sweet and savory dishes as well as adding superb flavour to ice cream and jams (gelées extra de thé).

A selection of such dishes can be sampled at the MARIAGE FRÈRES tea houses, all from recipes developed by the company.

For example:
- *Souchong Duck with Smoky Formosa Tea*
- *Chicken Supreme with Mild Spice Tea*
- *Salmon Steak with Green Matcha Tea*
- *Bavarois Cream with Tea from the High Plateaux of Ceylon*
- *Mount Fuji Mousse, with Green Matcha Tea*
- *Scones with Gelées Extra de Thé.*

TEA IN THE HOME

*T*O PREVENT A TEAPOT FROM acquiring a musty odour when not in use, place a lump of sugar or a spoonful of tea in the bottom. Do not replace the lid.

TO CLEAN A TEAPOT IN WHICH TEA HAS gone mouldy, wash it in very hot water (without detergent), then place several slices of lemon in the bottom and fill again with boiling water.

Allow to stand for 24 hours, by which time the odour will have vanished.

Alternately, replace the lemon slices with two soup spoons of mustard powder.

Stir well, rinse with boiling water, and dry thoroughly.

TO ELIMINATE TEA STAINS:

— if the stain is recent, rub with lemon or with warm, soapy water;

— if the fabric is wool or silk, mix an egg yolk with a little warm water, rub gently, rinse and dry;

— if the stain is old, sponge it with glycerol diluted in water.

TO RID A FRYING PAN OF THE ODOUR of fish or onion, rub it with damp tea leaves.

TO CLEAN PAINTED WOODWORK, nothing is as effective as strong tea.

TO CLEAN AND REVIVE THE COLOUR of carpets, scatter them with used tea leaves–well drained– then brush off.

SILK GARMENTS, TATAMIS AND other mats can be washed with tea, which removes stains and odours and gives them a fine sheen.

TO GIVE DOILIES AND lace a charming ochre colour, boil them with a handful of tea leaves.

TO MAKE UNMATCHED stockings match, dip them in very strong tea, which will give them a uniform golden colour.

USED TEA LEAVES CONSTITUTE excellent fertilizer for potted plants. They can be mixed into the soil with the aid of a fork.
Plants can also be watered from time to time with tea.

TO DRIVE MOSQUITOS FROM A ROOM, burn some tea leaves.

TEA AND BEAUTY

'Teaism is the art of concealing beauty that you may discover it, of suggesting what you dare not reveal.'

Okakura Kakuzo (1862-1913)
The Book of Tea

RINSING AUBURN HAIR IN TEA will give it wonderful coppery highlights.

Tea mixed with a few drops of lemon is an excellent astringent for oily skin.

Tea steeped in pure water with a lump of sugar can be used to soften the skin after cleansing or shaving.

It is also used in the East for personal hygiene.

Tea compresses on the eyelids reinvigorate tired eyes.

Tea can be dabbed onto face, neck, and even arms and legs to give a delicate tan to skin that has not yet been tanned, or to prolong a tan acquired on holiday.

TEA AND HEALTH

'Tea stimulates the humours and wise thoughts. Its refreshes the body and soothes the mind. If you are downhearted, tea will give you strength.'

Emperor Chen-Nung

*E*UROPEAN DOCTORS HAVE NOTED the beneficial effects of tea ever since the seventeenth century. In 1641, a Dutch physician named Nicolas Direks claimed in his Observationes Medicae that no other plant had such remarkable virtues, and that 'the habit of drinking tea preserves people from all kinds of sickness, insuring a long life'.

In 1678, another Dutch doctor, Cornelis Bontekoe, published a treatise on 'Tea, that Excellent Beverage' in which he listed its beneficial properties, translated from the Chinese:

The Power of Tea

Tea has the following virtues:

1. Purifies the blood

2. Expels heavy dreams

3. Relieves the mind of dark thoughts

4. Relieves and heals vertigo and headaches

5. Treats dropsy

6. Is an excellent remedy for catarrh

7. Dries all humidity

8. Cures constipation

9. Clears the sight

10. Protects from bad humours and liver disorders

11. Is a good remedy for all bladder trouble

12. Alleviates spleen maladies

13. Vanquishes drowsiness

14. Vanquishes dullness

15. Renders active and energetic

16. Renders courageous

17. Eliminates fear

18. Dissipates pain caused by colic

19. Is a good remedy for menstrual pains

20. Strengthens all internal parts

21. Sharpens the mind

22. Reinforces the memory

23. Reinforces intelligence

24. Purges bile

25. Reinforces sexual energy

26. Slakes thirst'

• Tea is healthy, beneficial, stimulating, diuretic, and alkaline.

Healthy

Tea leaves contain essential vitamins and mineral salts:
— notably vitamins A, B1, B2, B12, C (especially green tea), E, K, P, and PP,
— calcium, potassium, manganese, copper, zinc, nickel, and phosphoric acid, plus fluoride (helps prevent tooth decay),
— carotene and chlorophyll.

Stimulating

Tea stimulates, rather than excites. Both of its main components, theine and tannin, have marked stimulating effects. Theine has a remarkable effect on the brain and central nervous system. Tea efficiently stimulates intellectual activity and clearly alleviates fatigue.

Diuretic

The theine and theophylline in tea stimulate kidney functions. Tea has no calories, is salt free, dissolves fats, and aids digestion. Tea is perfect for salt-free diets.

Alkaline

Drunk in normal quantities, the alkaline components in tea help limit acidification of the human body.

Beneficial

Tea acts on the circulatory system. Chemists have confirmed the presence of theine and theophylline, which are cardiac, cerebral, and diuretic stimulants, as well as flavonoids, which inhibit cholesterol build-up and lower blood pressure. Tea also contains fluoride (three cups a day efficiently protects tooth enamel), catechins, which have antiseptic effects, and vitamin C (especially green teas). Tea is also perfect for health diets: it has no calories or salt, dissolves fats, and aids digestion.

• Medical Discoveries

Tea has a major anti-oxidising effect

(Dr. Prior, USDA Human Nutrition Research Center on Aging, Tufts University, and Dr. Cao, University of Connecticut at Storrs)

Tea is rich in natural compounds known as flavonols that act as anti-oxidants, neutralising free radicals that can damage the cells of the human body. Major studies have shown that tea's anti-oxidising power is superior to that of twenty-two fruits and vegetables.

In particular, the catechin present in tea is allegedly 100 times more efficient in neutralising free radicals than vitamin C, and twenty-five times more efficient than vitamin E. Simply drinking one cup of tea per day can make a major contribution to an individual's daily intake of anti-oxidants.

Green tea is highly recommended for expectant mothers

(Dr. Ichiro Mori, School of Medicine, University of Kagoshima)

Dr. Mori and his assistants have focused their research on the relationship between certain minerals such as zinc and copper, and premature birth of underweight babies. Whereas a regular green-tea drinker has a daily intake of roughly 30 mg of zinc, people who do not drink green tea have an intake of less than 15 mg.

Expectant mothers have a particular need for zinc, since zinc is one of the essential nutrients required during pregnancy.

Green tea and the prevention of tooth decay

(Dr. Masao Onishi, Emeritus Professor, Tokyo School of Medicine and Dentistry)

After long years of research, Dr. Onishi concluded that a single cup of green tea per day would reduce by half the rate of tooth decay among children and adolescents. 'The simple act of rinsing the mouth after meals with green tea is a highly efficient preventative against tooth decay'. Dr. Onishi bases his conclusions on the role of fluoride in green tea, which actively fights tooth decay.

Tea apparently offers protection against several types of cancer

Dr. Junshi Chen, of the Chinese Academy of Preventive Medicine in Beijing, has developed a cancer treatment involving a combination of components of black and green tea, administered orally, which allegedly leads to a significant improvement in clinical signs of mouth cancer and inhibits the proliferation of pre-cancerous cells.
Several reports have discussed the chemio-preventive effects of tea (Dr. Fung-Lung Chung, American Health Foundation): drinking green and black tea supposedly slows the spread of lung cancers provoked by tobacco-linked carcinogens.
Two scientists from the National Cancer Institute have published data that would seem to link tea drinking to a lower risk of cancers of the digestive tract and elsewhere, as well as pre-clinical trials suggesting that green and black teas have preventive effects on pre-cancerous cells.

THE ART OF MAKING FINE TEA

Tea is a noble beverage. Tea making is an art which combines experience with tradition.

As with wine, 'vintage' harvests are the pride of famous estates, the mere names of which are highly esteemed by connoisseurs. The beverage, however, requires preparation. Deciding on water, teapot, and steeping time are all steps in appreciating tea's quintessential qualities–if mishandled, its lustre is damaged. That is why it is important to pay very special attention to the following advice on selecting utensils and preparing tea. It is the fruit of long experience.

THE ART OF SELECTING WATER

*T*HE PRIMARY ELEMENT IN determining the flavour and aroma of tea is the water in which the leaves are steeped. The wrong water will ruin the flavour of the finest tea.

From time immemorial, tea masters have taken great care in selecting the right water.

According to Lu Yu's Cha King, mountain water is the best, followed by river water and spring water

Indeed, the delicate tea plant requires very pure, neutral water.
It should not be too hard or contain undesirable elements like chlorine, lead, calcium oxide, and magnesium.

Salty, ferrous, or chlorinated water is inappropriate and should never be used for making tea.

The water should be tasteless. If local tap water is not right for fine teas, then use mineral water or neutral spring water.

'Drapé': A MARIAGE FRÈRES reproduction of a 16th-century Chinese teapot.

THE ART OF SELECTING A TEAPOT

*'The path to heaven
passes by a teapot'.*
            Ancient proverb

*T*EA APPRECIATION
should produce
aesthetic pleasure, thanks
primarily to the equipage
used. Often considered
veritable works of art, it
reflects the mood or state of
mind of the person serving
the tea. Great attention
should therefore be paid to it.

— FOR MILD, DELICATE AND FRAGRANT
teas such as Formosa Oolong,
Darjeeling, and China tea, select a
teapot with a smooth inner surface
of china, porcelain, glass, or
enamelled cast-iron.

● Cast-iron teapots reflect eight
centuries of Japanese tradition.
They were once noble objects
presented to lords–the solid, highly
resistant material was a symbol of
strength and authority.
They retain heat perfectly.
Since the inside is lined with enamel,
they can be used for all kinds of tea.
A strainer is incorporated, making it
easy to control the steeping time.
They are ideal teapots.

● Porcelain teapots are also perfectly

suited for enhancing the natural
taste of tea.

● Glass teapots are recommended for
flavoured teas, since they retain no
trace of odour, making it possible to
go from one flavour to another.

— FOR STRONGER TEAS RICH IN TANNIN,
such as those from Ceylon, Assam,
Indonesia, South America, Oceania,
and Africa, use a teapot in porous
terracotta or in a metal like pewter or
silver.

● A Chinese Yixing teapot, in
unenamelled terracotta, originally from
the province of Jiangsu, is considered
ideal. It is soon 'broken in' when a
thin deposit forms, allowing the tea to
develop its full flavour.
But once a teapot has been broken
in it should never be used for
another type of tea.

Ideally, several teapots should be on hand:

— one for black, matured and blue teas.

— another for smoky teas.

— a third for flavoured teas.

— a fourth for green, yellow or white teas.

It is preferable to use a teapot with a built-in strainer; if not, it is essential to buy a baggy cotton strainer known as a 'Tea Taster Filter'. The tea leaves will not release their full flavour if squeezed into a small infuser.

The teapot should be rinsed with clean water, turned upside down to drain, then dried outside. A teapot should never be washed with the rest of the dishes.

A teapot should be used solely for tea, and never for anything else.

THE ART OF PREPARING TEA

The way tea is prepared has evolved through three main stages, associated with three historical schools in China:

Boiled Tea: Tang Dynasty (618–907 AD.)
Whipped Tea: Song Dynasty (960–1279 AD.)
Steeped Tea: Ming Dynasty (1368–1644 AD.)

• *The school of boiled tea:*
Tang Dynasty *(618-907 AD.)*

During the Tang dynasty, tea was pressed into bricks or cakes.

Lu Yu, the bard of brick tea, elevated the beverage to the realm of poetry. Drinking tea became one of the elegant pastimes of the day.

Since bricks of compressed tea were easy to export, tea began to spread toward Mongolia and Tibet in the tenth century.

The oldest tea routes, then, were the ones linking northern China to Mongolia and southwestern China to Tibet.

Caravans of camels and yaks took three and a half months to transport the precious cakes of tea some 1,000 miles, occasionally at altitudes of over 16,000 feet.

The Tibetan art

The art of boiled tea

Tibetans still practice their traditional art. To make tea, they crush a cake of tea in a mortar, then boil it with rice, ginger, orange peel, spices, milk, and sometimes onions.

To prepare compressed tea, crumble a little piece of the cake (approximately two grams per cup), and boil it in water for about three minutes. Stir, pour through a strainer, and serve.

• The school of whipped tea: Song Dynasty (960–1279 AD.)

During the Song dynasty, tea came in powdered form.

As the art of fine living took on new meaning, tea became more than just an elegant pastime.

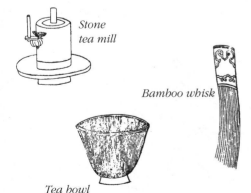

Stone tea mill

Bamboo whisk

Tea bowl

The cult of tea evolved into one of the paths toward enlightenment.

Zen Buddhists of the southern rite developed an entire ritual of tea, which gave birth to Cha No Yu, the tea ceremony as later developed in Japan.

The Japanese art

Cha No Yu, an art of ritualized hospitality.

Tea ceremony, Japan, 1880.

The origins of the Cha No Yu, or tea ceremony, were Chinese and religious, but it was in fifteenth-century Japan that the ritual was codified. Several schools then emerged, but it was the followers of the famous tea master Rikyu who permanently established the rules in the sixteenth century.

This highly respected method of attaining awareness of self and others has been handed down from generation to generation as the pillar and soul of Japanese culture. It greatly influences the way the Japanese treat tea even today, for Cha No Yu is still a ritualized art of hospitality.

Each cup of whipped tea is prepared separately, using green Matcha tea. Place about 1.5 grams in a bowl, then pour in 4 centilitres (slightly less than 1.5 fluid oz) of hot water (80°C / 170°F). Swiftly whip the tea for 30 seconds with a bamboo whisk, or chasen, then drink it.

• The school of steeped tea: Ming Dynasty (1368-1644 AD.)

During the Ming dynasty, tea was used in leaf form.

A few tea leaves were placed in a chung, or small bowl with cover, followed by simmering water.
The cover was then set on the bowl and the tea left to steep.

Europe only discovered tea at the end of the Ming dynasty, and so it adopted the school of steeped tea.

out the essence of its aroma and flavour. Most of the utensils used in Gongfu Cha date back to the Song dynasty (10th – 13th century).

To make steeped tea, first heat the utensils. Then pour simmering water over leaves of fine quality tea, which may be green, black, or–quite often–blue tea like Ti Kuan Yin and Tung Ting.

The tea is steeped in a tiny pot, which means that it is much more concentrated than ordinary tea, and should be savoured like a liqueur. It is drunk from very small cups.

The Chinese method entails an art of creating a moment of relaxed conviviality, sharing an exquisite drink in a pleasant setting.

The Chinese art

Gongfu Cha, an art of convivial spontaneity.

Unlike the Japanese tea ceremony, Gongfu Cha does not involve an ideal quest or respect for a highly codified ritual.

Tea must nevertheless be prepared in meticulous fashion in order to bring

The Russian art

The samovar, symbol of hospitality.

In Russia, tea is a beverage that warms both heart and body. The term for 'tip' in Russian is 'na chaï', which means 'for a cup of tea'.

As Russia's popular national beverage, tea is always ready whenever family or guests drop by, thanks to the famous samovar.
A samovar is not a teapot but a cauldron that keeps water at just the right temperature so that tea can be made at a moment's notice.

To drink Russian-style tea, make extremely concentrated tea in a small teapot (half water, half tea). Whenever you want a cup of tea, pour a drop of concentrated tea in the bottom of a cup, then add hot water from the samovar. The little teapot is placed on top of the samovar, and kept warm by the steam.

In Russia, a lump of sugar is placed in the mouth to sweeten the tea as it fills the palate.

Other traditional methods of drinking tea include adding jam, cream, or honey.

The French art
French connoisseurship: the art of perfect elegance according to Mariage Frères.

The fundamental concepts of the French school are perfect elegance and taste, as refined during several centuries of tradition. Its principles, laid down by the ancestors of the MARIAGE family, are still respected by France's premier Tea House.

French drink the widest variety of teas in the world, ranging from 50 of the most reputable Darjeeling estates to mild Gyokuro tea, not forgetting Malawi teas and the rarest blends.

Green tea, white tea, black tea, red tea, blue tea, matured tea, and flavoured tea are all part of an unrivalled palette available to French connoisseurs. French tea connoisseurs are highly aware of the subtle differences between teas—whether ordinary, rare or fancy—choosing those most appropriate in the morning, at meal time, for a tea break, for afternoon tea, or in the evening.

Full attention is required to appreciate and recognize the distinct personality of various teas, selecting and preparing each one in just the right way, not only releasing its unique flavour but also choosing the right moment to appreciate it.

Just like French wine, combining tea with various dishes is a high art. Serving it in refined tea services is also part of any festive occasion. Every detail should delight both eye and palate. French connoisseurs expect leaves to be attractive, packaging to be lavish, flavour to be intact.

Over the years, the art of developing blends has yielded unique teas that are now available in fine shops in London, New York, and Tokyo, where they are prestigiously known as 'French tea'.

Another universally recognized aspect of French connoisseurship, epitomized by MARIAGE FRÈRES, involves the reproduction of traditional tea services, the appreciation of ancient tea caddies, and the design of modern utensils.

Tea has become a part of French gastronomy, and now graces the menus of the greatest chefs.

MARIAGE FRÈRES' traditional savoir-faire concerning tea is now respected even in Japan.

Careful steeping: the cornerstone of the French method. The French school features very careful preparation, concern for quality, and a marked interest for teas grown on a specific estate (which yields a fine vintage). Every tea has its special features, its specific nature, its secrets. The water temperature and steeping time that bring out those features are also specific, and must be respected.

An initial obstacle on the path to perfection is confusion between steeping time and the 'strength' of tea. Steeped tea releases all its theine, or stimulant, in three minutes.

Tea given by French Empress Eugénie in the 'Chinese Salon' of Compiègne Château, late 19th century.

After that time, it is the somewhat bitter tannins that are released which, when mixed with theine, give tea its full flavour.

The longer tea is steeped, the more tannin there is and the less active the theine becomes. That means it is more stimulating if steeped less. Be careful, however not to let tea steep too long (especially black tea in the form of broken leaves or fannings), because it can become too bitter to drink.

Water temperature

The secret of successful tea inevitably entails carefully monitoring the temperature of the water. Water should barely simmer, at a temperature of 95–98°C (203–208°F). Extended boiling 'kills' water and damages tea leaves, harming aroma and flavour.

The temperature should be lower for white and green teas (the finer the quality, the lower the temperature). Simmered water should thus be allowed to cool to 70°C (158°F), which is the perfect temperature for rare white and green teas.

Sugar, milk, and lemon

In general, purists drink fine teas plain, without milk, sugar, or lemon. Should you wish to sweeten your tea anyway, use special sugar that neither denatures nor alters the taste of tea.

It is perfectly acceptable to add a drop of cold milk to teas from Ceylon, Assam, south India, Indonesia, South America, Oceania, and Africa, especially when they come in the form of broken leaves or fannings.

Lemon, however, changes the nature of tea. It can be advantageously replaced by a slice of orange.

Iced tea

MARIAGE FRÈRES recommend two methods to prepare iced tea:

First method, for a stronger taste.

- Put about 10 grams (1/3 oz) tea or 4 caddy spoons into a tea pot.
- Cover with half a litre (1 pint) of simmering water.
- Let infuse 3 to 5 minutes according to the type of tea.
- Take out the tea leaves and pour the hot tea into glasses filled with ice cubes.

Second method, for a lighter taste, like scented water.

- Put about 10 grams (1/3 oz) of tea or 4 caddy spoons into a tea pot.
- Cover with one litre (2 pints) of water at room temperature.
- Keep the tea pot into the refrigerator for 12 hours.
- Take out the tea leaves and serve. You may add sugar cane syrup according to your taste.

Mariage Frères' Five Golden Rules
for Making Tea Successfully

Black teas, matured teas, blue teas, and flavoured teas:

1 - Pre-heat the teapot, after inserting the tea strainer or filter,* by rinsing it with boiling water.

2 - Place a teaspoon of tea (roughly 2.5 g) per cup in the warm strainer* and let it stand for a few moments, allowing the steam to begin developing the leaves' aroma.

3 - Pour simmering water on the tea so that all the leaves are covered.

4 - Let the tea steep (refer to chart):
- about 2 minutes for fannings
- about 3 minutes for broken leaf teas
- about 5 minutes for whole leaf teas
- barely 3 minutes for first flush Darjeeling (slightly increasing the amount of tea to 3.5 g per cup)
- 7 minutes for blue teas.

5 - It is then essential to remove the strainer or filter* containing the leaves. The tea must then be stirred (another important step) and finally poured. Teas from great gardens should not be drunk too hot; let them stand a few moments after steeping, so that the palate can better appreciate the most subtle of fragrances.

White and green teas:

1 - Pre-heat the pot or chung (cup with cover) as above.

2 - Place the appropriate amount of tea per person or cup (refer to chart). Let the leaves stand for a few moments to allow the steam to begin developing the aroma.

3 - Pour hot water onto the tea (refer to chart for exact temperature).

4 - Let the tea steep (refer to chart):
- 1 to 3 minutes for green tea
- 15 minutes for white Yin Zhen
- 7 minutes for white Pai Mu Tan.

5 - Remove the tea leaves, stir, and serve.

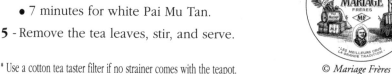

* Use a cotton tea taster filter if no strainer comes with the teapot.   © *Mariage Frères*

Mariage Frères' Steeping Chart

TEA	AMOUNT OF TEA	WATER TEMPERATURE	AMOUNT OF WATER *	STEEPING TIME
WHITE TEA YIN ZHEN	5 G	70°C/158°F	20 CL	15 MN
WHITE TEAS PAI MU TAN	5 G	85°C/185°F	20 CL	7 MN
FINEST GREEN TEAS	5 G	70°C/185°F	20 CL	3 MN
GREEN TEAS	5 G	95°C/203°F	20 CL	3 MN
GYOKURO N° T414	10 G	50°C/122°F	6 CL	2,5 MN

This tea should be prepared in tiny quantities and drunk from minuscule cups. It can be steeped three times.

TEA	AMOUNT OF TEA	WATER TEMPERATURE	AMOUNT OF WATER *	STEEPING TIME
GREEN JAPAN TEAS T416 T417 T418 T419 T4273 T4274 T4275 T4276 T4277 T4283	6,5 G	70°C/158°F	20 CL	2 MN
GREEN JAPAN TEAS T421 T424 T426	4,5 G	90°C/194°F	20 CL	1 to 2 MN
GREEN JAPAN TEAS T420 T422 T425	4,5 G	95°C/203°F	20 CL	1 MN
BLUE TEAS	2,5 G	95°C/203°F	20 CL	7 MN
DARJEELING FIRST FLUSH	3,5 G	95°C/203°F	20 CL	3 MN
WHOLE LEAF MATURED TEAS AND BLACK TEAS	2,5 G	95°C/203°F	20 CL	5 MN
BROKEN LEAF BLACK TEAS BOP and BPS AND BLACK PEKOE TEAS	2,5 G	95°C/203°F	20 CL	3 MN
BLACK TEAS IN FANNINGS BOPF	2,5 G	95°C/203°F	20 CL	2 MN
FLAVOURED TEAS	2,5 G	95°C/203°F	20 CL	3 to 5 MN

* 20 cl of water is approximately 7 fluid ounces, or about one cup.

THE ART OF STORING TEA

*T*EA IS A DELICATE SUBSTANCE. Its fragrance is marvellous and subtle. Treat it with the respect it deserves, and it will more than pay you back for such attention. Great care has been taken in storing tea from time immemorial.

In the eighteenth century, tea was an aristocratic beverage, a rare colonial import sold in Europe at extravagant prices. It was often kept in tea 'caddies' (from the Malay word 'kati', a unit weighing about one pound) which were small casks made of precious wood, often veritable works of art. The mistress of the house would lock the caddy with a key in order to avoid leading her servants into temptation.

• Precautions

Air, light, heat, and dampness are tea's natural enemies.

Tea easily absorbs the humidity and odours of the place where it is stored. It is also affected by external conditions of light and temperature.

It should not be left in a place that is too dry or too damp.

It is better to avoid contact with food or other products that might leave an odour or alter its quality (notably spices, coffee, and other scented or medicinal products).

Tea also deteriorates if exposed to light. That is why it should not be kept in a transparent container.

Proper storage requires a traditional tea caddy, a metallic or double-sealed can, or other ceramic pot or hermetically-sealed container.

The container should be clean, dry, and odour-free.

A tea container, like a teapot, should never be used for any other purpose.

• Length of Storage

Contrary to popular belief, certain teas can be stored for a long time, provided that the above rules are strictly followed.

In China, vintage harvests are highly valued by connoisseurs and are sold at high prices, notably matured or Pu-Erh teas.

They are carefully stored, sometimes for as long as fifty years, and their storage is attentively and regularly monitored throughout that time.

Their leaves are regularly heated, a technique that requires highly specific skills.

Conventional teas can be stored for approximately two years. As to flavoured teas, storage life is generally about twelve months.

'Tea, though ridiculed by those who are naturally coarse in their sensibilities... will always be the favoured beverage of the intellectual'

Thomas de Quincey (1785 - 1859)
Confessions of an Opium Eater.

Tea plantations across the world

THE BOOK OF TEA

' *W hen will the West understand, or try to understand, the East?*
Strangely enough, humanity has so far met in the tea-cup.
It is the only Asiatic ceremonial which commands universal esteem'.

Okakura Kakuzo (1862-1913)
The Book of Tea

CLASSIFYING TEAS

The oldest tea plant in the world – the "king of tea trees" – can apparently be found on the Mountain of Fragrant Bamboo near Xiaowan in the Chinese province of Yunnan. The plant is allegedly 3,200 years old.

Tea tasting, China, late 19th century.

THE TEA PLANT, THEA SINENSIS, comes from Asia and is part of the camellia family, Camellia Sinensis. In its wild state, it is a tree that can grow quite tall.

When constantly pruned, it remains a bush that produces pointed young buds.

It is these young buds that are the source of tea.

The tea plant requires a warm, wet climate and well-drained soil. It grows well at altitudes up to 9,000 feet.

Like vintage wines, each tea crop reflects local characteristics–the nature of the soil, the climate, the amount of sun and rain, the time of plucking.

All teas come from the same plant. Once harvested, however, the way the leaves are processed determines the type of tea obtained.

Mariage Frères divide tea into eight general categories: white, green, yellow, blue, black, matured, compressed, and flavoured.

1. White Teas

White tea, originally produced in China's Fujian Province, is unique.

It is different from all other teas in that the fresh leaves undergo only two processing operations, in a rigourously natural fashion: withering and drying.

Very little white tea is produced, and its manufacture requires particular care.

The name 'white' tea comes from the silvery-white colour of its leaves, which often have a white down on them.

Two major varieties of white tea exist:
● Yin Zhen ('Silver Needles'),
● Pai Mu Tan ('White Peony').

China is practically the only supplier of high quality white teas.

2. Green Teas

Green tea is unoxidised tea.

It results from a special preparation designed to prevent the natural oxidation process.

There are two main ways to produce green tea:

Chinese Method

The freshly plucked leaves are roasted in heated copper basins over a fire maintained at a temperature of 100°C (212°F). Examples include Lung Ching, Chun Mee, and Gunpowder.

Japanese Method

The leaves are immediately sweated in a steam tank (this is how Sencha, among other teas, is produced).

The leaves thereby become soft and pliable enough to roll; they are partially rolled by hand and then dried.

This operation is repeated several times. Then, after a final drying, the leaves are sorted into various categories. The different qualities of green tea depend on colour, appearance, and fragrance.

China, Formosa, and Japan are the main producers of green tea.

● *Powdered green tea:*

In Japan, a powdered green tea called Matcha is often used for the Cha No Yu tea ceremony. After being dried with hot air and then sweated, the leaves are chopped into tiny pieces (tencha) and dried once again. Then they are ground into powder by a millstone.

3. Yellow Teas

Yellow tea has been a Chinese speciality since the sixteenth century.

It is made from green tea: leaves are

placed in storage once the oxidation process has been halted, and the phenol they contain soon automatically oxidises to give the leaves - and the liquor - a mild, savoury bouquet. They display a unique, as yet unexplained, characteristic: initially green, the leaves become yellow during the natural maturing process, and keep this hue until they are steeped.
A distinction is traditionally made between small-leaf yellow teas (composed of young shoots) and larger-leaf yellow teas.

4. Blue Teas

Blue tea represents a half-way stage between green and black tea.
The leaves undergo brief oxidation. Blue tea is usually called Oolong, which means 'black dragon', and occasionally Bohea (or Bohe or even Bou), which is a deformation of Wu Yi, the name of the famous mountain in China's Fujian Province where the most highly esteemed blue tea is made.

There are two major methods of producing blue tea:

Chinese Method

Oxidation does not exceed 12 to 15%. These teas are thought by the Chinese to be the most beneficial, endowed with the best virtues.

Formosa Method

Known abroad as Oriental Beauty ('Ming-Tê', or 'Brilliant Virtue' on Formosa itself), this tea undergoes

60 to 70% of the oxidation process, making it close to black tea. Formosa tea is highly renowned in both France and the United States.

Blue tea combines the sweet scent of green tea with the delicate aroma of black tea.

5. Black Teas

Black tea is completely oxidised.

In the standard or 'orthodox' method, black tea undergoes five basic operations:

withering, rolling, oxidation, drying, and sorting.

Experts generally grade teas according to the appearance of the leaves.

These grades do not necessarily indicate quality–broken-leaf tea and even fannings will be of the same quality as whole-leaf tea assuming they are produced from the same leaves.

Whole-leaf tea

The term Orange Pekoe has a double etymology:

— 'Orange' signifies royal, from the House of Orange, Holland's royal family.

— 'Pekoe' comes from the Chinese Pak-Ho ('hair' or 'down') because the buds are covered with a light, white down.

Flowery Orange Pekoe

Orange Pekoe

Pekoe

Pekoe Souchong

Souchong

© *Mariage Frères*

● *F.O.P.: Flowery Orange Pekoe*

Refers to tea harvested from the terminal bud and first leaf of each shoot. These teas are composed of young, tender, finely rolled leaves, with a greater or lesser proportion of 'tips'.

The presence of the tip of the bud is a sign of quality, since only the youngest shoots are used for the finest teas.

These shoots terminate in two leaves and a tiny bud.

During the rolling process, which releases the leaves' essential oils, the furry buds absorb the oils and thereby acquire all their aroma and colour (golden or silver).

● *G.F.O.P.: Golden Flowery Orange Pekoe*
F.O.P. with golden tips.

● *T.G.F.O.P.: Tippy Golden Flowery Orange Pekoe*
F.O.P. with a high proportion of golden tips.

● *F.T.G.F.O.P.: Finest Tippy Golden Flowery Orange Pekoe*
F.O.P. of outstanding quality.

● *S.F.T.G.F.O.P.: Special Finest Tippy Golden Flowery Orange Pekoe*
The finest F.O.P. available.

● *O.P.: Orange Pekoe*
Characterized by long leaves, somewhat longer than Flowery Orange Pekoe (F.O.P.), rolled lengthwise, needle-like. The plucking takes place once the terminal bud has evolved into a leaf. Thus O.P. rarely contains tips.

● *P.: Pekoe*
Shorter, less fine leaves with no tips.

● *F.P.: Flowery Pekoe*
Leaves specially rolled into a ball.

● *P.S.: Pekoe Souchong*
Somewhat coarser leaves.

- *S.: Souchong*
Large leaves rolled lengthwise.
Often used for smoky China teas.
Specialists also add the number '1'
to a grade if it is the finest quality
within that grade.
For example, F.T.G.F.O.P.1, O.P.1, etc.

Broken-Leaf tea

Broken-leaf teas come from the fragile parts of the leaf. Whole leaves are often deliberately broken to obtain such teas.
They are marketed in the following grades:

- *G.F.B.O.P.: Golden Flowery Broken Orange Pekoe*
- *G.B.O.P.: Golden Broken Orange Pekoe*
- *T.G.B.O.P.: Tippy Golden Broken Orange Pekoe*
- *F.B.O.P.: Flowery Broken Orange Pekoe*
- *B.O.P. : Broken Orange Pekoe*
- *B.P.S. : Broken Pekoe Souchong*

Fannings

Not to be confused with dust, fannings are leaves that are broken into tiny flat pieces (1 to 1.5 mm).
Fannings make stronger tea than ordinary broken leaves.

They are generally labelled:

- *B.O.P.F.: Broken Orange Pekoe Fannings*

Those who like strong tea should chose Broken, Pekoe and Fannings grades. Others, who prefer more subtle tea, should chose Flowery Orange Pekoe or Orange Pekoe.

6. Matured Teas

Matured teas were developed in the early Tang dynasty (618-907 CE.) They differ from black tea in their specific preparation, requiring successive stages of a very long fermentation process in cellars specially designed for this aging.

The longer it is kept, the more a matured tea's fragrance will develop and acquire depth, even as the level of theine drops significantly. The resulting teas are totally mild, with no harshness or bitterness, and their flavour steadily gains in subtlety, yielding some of the rarest and most sought-after teas.

Matured teas are unique, for they are the only ones that improve with time; certain fifty- and sixty-year-old teas are highly prized by true connoisseurs.

7. Compressed Teas

The name of Pu-Erh is generally given to various forms of tea compressed into bricks or cakes, notably those from Yunnan.

Pu-Erh may also be sold in non-compressed form.

These teas are sometimes called Bian-Xiao Cha, which means 'tea for beyond the border'. It has been a Chinese specialty ever since the Tang dynasty, and still represents 20% of the country's total production. Compressed tea is produced in the provinces of Guang Xi, Hunan, Hu Bei, Szechwan, and Yunnan.

The leaves of matured, green, black, blue or flavoured tea are pressed into molds, which yield various types of brick or cake. Those most common in Europe are:
- Dschuan Cha, brick of black tea;
- Tuo Cha, bird's nest from Yunnan;
- Pu-Erh square brick from Yunnan;
- Pu-Erh Beeng Cha, flat cake of tea.

Pu-Erh teas are known for their healing virtues.

8. Flavoured Teas

The combination of tea with a specific flavour.

The Chinese often add a fragrance that provides a g the tea's own aroma.There are three major types of flavoured teas:

Grand Classic Scents

Mainly used with China teas (black, white, green or blue), the leaves are mixed with parts of other plants having a specific scent–jasmine, rose, orchid, and orange flower are the most prestigious.
The flowers must be picked at just the right moment, before they have completely blossomed.

While jasmine teas are the most popular, the most successful scent is probably essence of bergamot (a citrus oil), used in Earl Grey. The recipe was confided by a Chinese mandarin to Earl Grey, the British Prime Minister, who launched the tea in England.

Fancy Teas

After learning how to flavour tea from the Chinese, European merchants decided to broaden the range of scents in the 1950s:

– initially, they used local fruit and flowers, which led to apricot tea, raspberry tea, black currant tea, and so on,

– later, they employed spices and exotic fruit and flowers, yielding vanilla tea, mango tea, etc.

Flavoured Blends

Around 1970, flavoured teas became enormously popular in continental Europe. Tea merchants then began combining various scents to produce special blends such as Tropical, which employs various tropical fruits.

THE FINEST HARVESTS

The finest quality leaves should 'crease like the leathern boots of Tatar horsemen, curl like the dewlap of a mighty bullock, unfold like a mist rising out of a ravine, gleam like a lake touched by a zephyr, and be wet and soft like fine earth newly swept by rain'.

Lu Yu (733-804)
Cha King, (Holy Scripture of Tea)
The first book devoted to tea

CHINA

Tea is one of the most precious gifts China has ever offered to the world.

Tea House, China, late 19th century

EA HAS PLAYED A MAJOR ROLE IN Chinese foreign trade for over a thousand years.

Tea is grown manually in China. Plucked and processed in a careful, systematic manner, China tea is known for its highly special colour, aroma, and flavour.

Production is limited to the temperate zones of the subtropical regions, where the climate is mild and rain abundant.

China produces the largest variety of teas in the world: white, green, yellow, blue, black, smoky, matured, flavoured, crafted, and compressed.

The main producing regions are located in the centre and south of the country: Shanghai, Jiangsu, Zhejiang, Ningbo, Anhui, Fujian, Jiang Xi, Henan, Hu Bei, Hunan, Guangdong, Guang Xi, Szechwan, Chongqing, Gui Zhou, Yunnan, and Hainan.

In general, tea cooperatives in each region control the blending of tea to produce reliable quality. That is why China teas, unlike those of India and Ceylon, are not marketed according the name of the estate. Instead, they are labelled according to taste and quality.

In rare cases, special harvests have retained their own name, giving them a reputation equal to that of French wines. The most glamorous teas remain the prerogative of a handful of connoisseurs and important officials. They are jealously guarded and rarely exported.

After sustained effort, Mariage Frères has obtained the privilege of importing the most exclusive and delicate teas. The company is thereby able to offer the most complete and precious range of rare teas anywhere.

• White China Teas

HITE TEA DATES BACK TO THE early Song dynasty of imperial China. True white teas are highly rare today. The major producing areas are within Fujian Province, namely Fuding, Zhenghe, Songqi, and Jiangyang Counties.

White tea is perfect for summer–highly refreshing, it lowers the internal temperature of the human body.

T2301 YIN ZHEN
'Silver Needles'
The height of perfection in white tea. The so-called 'imperial' plucking is done exclusively by hand on just two days of the year, when only the finest young buds are selected.
The marvellous leaves of Yin Zhen resemble needles covered by silvery tips, and yield a crystalline, pale mandarin liquor with the subtle, fresh fragrance of buds.
It is the most glamorous and costly white tea on earth.

T2302 PAI MU TAN IMPÉRIAL
This fabulous 'Imperial White Peony', from Fuding County in Fujian Province, is nobility itself.
Its fine, jade leaves have a high proportion of silver-needle tips, or Yin Zhen.
The flowery, crystalline liquor of Pai Mu Tan has a lively aroma and smooth taste.
A fabulous afternoon tea.

T2306 GRAND PAI MU TAN
'Honourable White Peony'
Silvery-green leaves of great beauty, with a subtle, flowery taste. Yields a mandarin-coloured liquor. A grand daytime tea.

T2307 PAI MU TAN
'White Peony'
White tea with great character, plus a fine, flowery aroma. Delightful in the evening.

• *Green China Teas*

Perles de thé

Bouquets de thé

Étoiles de thé

Bourgeons de thé

Crafted China teas

GREEN TEA GOES BACK A VERY long way in China.
For hundreds of years, only green tea existed–other types of tea came later.

Green tea is preferably grown in hilly or mountainous regions often covered in mist.

The various qualities of green tea are distinguished on the basis of colour, overall appearance, and fragrance.
The leaves of a brilliant green tea produce a clear, highly delicate liquor.

There are two types of green China tea: crafted tea and leaf tea.

Crafted Green China Teas

The most noble of Chinese traditions combines subtle taste with visual delight.

To this end, leaves are hand-crafted into bouquets that evoke stars, flowerbuds, or precious pearls.
Thanks to the clarity of the liquor, connoisseurs can appreciate the beauty of the composition in the bottom of the teacup.

T2200   BOUQUET DE THÉ VERT

This sculpted 'Bouquet of Green Tea' is a unique work of art from Huang Shan, the famous Yellow Mountain in Anhui Province.
The most tender, silvery-green leaves of Huang Shan Maofeng tea are hand-tied into a bouquet that resembles a green peony.
A delight to the eye as well as the palate, a bouquet steeped for three minutes in a chung (bowl with cover) yields a fine, pale, highly fragrant liquor with exquisite taste.
A magnificent tea for painters and poets.

T2213   BOURGEON DE THÉ

'Tea Bud' is an imperial legacy.
The most tender tea buds from the high mountains of Hu Bei province are selected by hand according to age-old methods from the days of the Chinese empire.
The silvery-green buds open in the cup like a lotus–the flower of Buddha–releasing the most delicate of fragrances.

Its subtle, incomparable flavour requires 4 minutes of steeping in very pure water at 85°C (185°F). A most distinguished taste, the height of refinement, will then fill the entire palate.

T2214 ÉTOILE DE THÉ

The 'Star of Tea' is another example of imperial art. Fine young jade-green buds from Hu Bei Province are fashioned into a gem-like 'star'. Two stars per cup should be steeped for 5 minutes in pure water at a temperature of 85°C (185°F). Their precious fragrance and subtle flavour will amaze the finest palates. A poetic beverage for the evening. May this star of tea light your way on the path toward serenity!

T2215 THÉ DE LA BONNE ÉTOILE

'Lucky Star' tea is a masterpiece of hand-crafting. Shaped into a star, it makes a thoughtful gift which brings good luck. The tea is pure, flowery, velvety, and extremely light with a hint of mandarin orange. The pinnacle of grace. Five stars per cup.

T2216 DRAGON DE FEU

'Fire Dragon' is enchanting. Like a dragon's fire-spitting tongue, it represents vitality, strength and energy. Its large leaves open in a chung like a majestic bouquet, yielding a refreshing drink. One piece per cup suffices.

Green China Leaf Teas

Hunan Province

T230 GOZHANG MAOJIAN

One of the ten most famous China teas. Grown in the high mountains of Hunan Province, it is notable for its long, downy leaves, pure aroma, and a delicate flavour that leaves a delicious after-taste. A subtle, daytime tea.

T238 AIGUILLES DE JADE

These 'Jade Needles' are unique. Highly precious buds are picked for a jade-coloured liquor with a slight taste of hazelnuts that stays long in the mouth. The mild, enveloping flavour is as peaceful as a dappled wood in spring. An unforgettable cup of tea that transports you to heavenly paradise.

Anhui Province

T2211 TAIPING HOUKUI

A treasure from Anhui, this famous green tea has a well-merited international reputation. Both its appearance and scent are unique. Its downy leaves are a handsome dark green. Once steeped, they slowly open to create a ravishing contrast with the pale green liquor. Its has a pronounced scent of orchids and a fully developed flavour. A subtle afternoon tea.

T2221 JIUHUA MAOFENG

This imperial tea is grown on Jihua Mountain in Anhui.

Its long, fine leaves yield a luminous, slightly sweet liquor with intense aroma. A grand daytime tea.

'Marco Polo' Teapot.

T2222 HUANG SHAN MAO FENG

This majestic green tea, one of the most famous in China, comes from Yellow Mountain. Legend has it that inconsolable tears of a beautiful young girl who worked on a tea plantation came down in such a steady rain that the body of her lover - whom fate had separated from her - was turned into a tea bush. This tale explains the perpetual mist that covers the area. The leaves, picked very young with their buds, are yellow-green, flat, and covered by silvery tips. The cup is apricot-coloured, its grand fragrance being simultaneously mild and highly flowery. This outstanding drink is the emperor of green teas.

Jiangsu Province

T220 PI LO CHUN

'Spiral Jade of Spring'

Pi Lo Chun is one of the rarest teas in the world. It is grown on the summit of Tung Ting Mountain near Tai Hu Lake in Jiangsu Province.

This extremely refined tea is noted for its round body, verdant hue, mild aroma, clear liquor, and pale, harmonious leaves. A truly grand tea for truly grand occasions.

T2225 YIXING CHA

Treasure of Yixing, grown on the high mountains surrounding the town of Yixing, itself known for its terracotta teapots.

This legendary green tea testifies to the ancestral art of tea.

Harvested only in the month of May, this spring tea is famous for its long, handsome leaves of emerald green, as well as for its penetrating aroma and sweet taste.

A sensual, evening tea.

Zhejiang Province

T2201 DONG YANG DONG BAI

Grown on the summit of Dong Bai Mountain in Zhejiang Province. This rare tea is reputed to be one of the finest green teas in the world. It is distinguished for its floral bouquet, its smooth taste, and its extremely clear liquor.

A divine tea for important celebrations.

T2202 PEI HOU

Grown at an altitude of 4000 feet, at the top of Tian Mu Mountain, in the Long Gang region.

Plucking is carefully done by hand just once a year, in spring.

A plucker must work for an entire day to obtain one kilogram of this famous tea. The tea is also processed entirely by hand, according to age-old traditions. The famous Pei Hou is noted for its fine, soft leaves of golden green, its subtle aroma, and its mild taste.
The garden can be reached only on foot, after a five-hour climb. The tea chests must descend by the same route on the shoulders of young men before beginning the long journey to France. A regal tea.

T221   LUNG CHING
'Dragon's Well'
Produced on the summits of the Tieh Mu Mountain chain, near the western lake of Hangzhow in Zhejiang. The garden boasts white sandy soil and a perfect climate for growing tea. Lung Ching's liquor resembles liquid jade, and has a delicious aroma that fills the palate with a delicate fragrance.
An ideal tea while reading.

T2210   PUITS DU DRAGON IMPÉRIAL
'Imperial Dragon's Well' is the most famous variety of Lung Ching. It is harvested prior to the Clear Light festival, before the spring rains arrive. Its quality is judged according to four criteria: golden green colour, sustained aroma, exquisite flavour, and leaves 'as flat as a sparrow's tongue'. Purists claim that it attains perfection when prepared with pure water from the Galloping Tigers spring, which emerges from the ground near a temple in the vicinity of the estate.

The most renowned green China tea in the world. A serene tea.

T223   HYSON
'Spring Flower'
Hyson owes its name to its fine young leaves, which are bright green in colour. Its yellow-green liquor has a pronounced, fresh fragrance and a velvety taste.

T2290   SENCHA ZHEJIANG
Prepared in Zhejiang Province according to Japanese methods, the leaves of this tea undergo a 'sweating' process immediately after plucking. It has an incomparable taste, simultaneously bitter and sweet. A perfect tea to accompany a meal.

T224   PINGSUEY GUNPOWDER
The youngest and most delicate leaves are carefully sorted and rolled to produce this tea, known for its fine golden-green liquor. A digestive tea.

T225   CHUN MEE
The name of this subtle tea evokes its resemblance to the human eyebrow. It is noted for its finesse, its clear green liquor, and its pure, strong, lasting aroma. A delicious basis for preparing green tea with mint.

T226   DRAGON BLANC
'White Dragon' is a heavenly nectar from Zhejiang. Its fine leaves are adorned with silver tips. Their flowery, morning-dew fragrance invades the palate and gives smooth, sweet, lasting pleasure even as it evolves into exquisite softness.

early as the third century BC. The tea is plucked in the mountains of Jiang Xi Province in the spring. Its pale green leaves have silver tips and give a fine golden-green liquor. A legendary tea.

T2205 MONTAGNE JIANG XI
'Jiang Xi Mountain' tea is characterized by its long, curly leaves with silver tips that yield a grand, flowery bouquet.

T2231 FEICUI
A famous tea from Jiang Xi Province. Its fine, distinguished, silvery leaves are carefully handled to give a sparkling liquor, sustained scent, and succulent flavour.
A refined beverage.

T228 MONTAGNE DU ROI
'King's Mountain' is mysterious. Grown on the high mountains of Zhejiang province, like the famous Lung Ching ('Dragon's Well'), its elegant leaves are 'as flat as a sparrow's tongue.'
Its aromatic flavour is gentle and delicate, like a bouquet of wild flowers.

T2300 SILVER DRAGON
Renowned as one of the most refined green China teas, Silver Dragon from Zhejiang Province is characterized by dragon-shaped leaves covered with a silvery-green down. Intense aroma, clear liquor, sweet flavour.
An imperial beverage.

Jiang Xi Province

T2203 THÉ DE L'EMPEREUR, LUSHAN YUNWU
Known as the preferred beverage of the Chinese imperial family, 'Emperor's Tea' was mentioned in Chinese literature as

Hu Bei Province

T222 XIA ZHOU BI FENG
The pride of famous Hu Bei teas. The leaves, plucked very young, are given special care. The liquor is limpid, producing a gentle fragrance and leaving a long, fresh, smooth taste in the mouth.
A relaxing tea.

T227 LONG ZHONG CUI LU
A tea of fine pedigree, with an orange-yellow liquor and highly pronounced aroma.
A subtle tea, appropriate when curling up with a book.

Guang Xi Province

T229   GUI HUA
A traditional Guang Xi tea subtly mixed with flowers of the bay tree. Very refined and refreshing.

T2303   WHITE DOWNY
A famous green tea called 'white' due to the colour of the fine down covering its leaves.
This Guang Xi tea is fresh yet refined and has a velvety taste.
Perfect for a relaxing tea break.

T2305   LIN YUN
A tea from Lin Yun County in Guang Xi Province. Like White Downy, the Chinese called this tea 'white' due to its appearance. Its fine, yellowish-green leaves produce a grand cup of tea, a mild and refreshing beverage all day long.

Other Provinces

T2223   DOUYUN MAOJIANG
The tender young leaves of this tea from the Douyun district of Gui Zhou Province are covered with a very fine down, and must be handled with particular care.
Their silvery forms recall dazzling snowflakes.
The clear liquor yields a gentle, smooth, sweet aroma.
A distinguished tea.

T2224   XINYANG MAOJIANG
This tea, from the high mountain region in southwestern Xin Yang County of Henan Province, is known for the way it is carefully plucked and processed.
It is characterized by fine downy leaves that are long and straight.
Its clear, jade-green liquor has a fresh, pronounced aroma and produces a long, smooth taste in the mouth.
An imperial beverage.

T2226   MONTAGNE KONG MING
Renowned for its broad, young, fragrant leaves, this green tea from the mountains of Yunnan Province is rarely encountered outside China.
It is noted for its celadon-and-gold liquor, its delicate aroma, and its mild taste.
A tea for reveries.

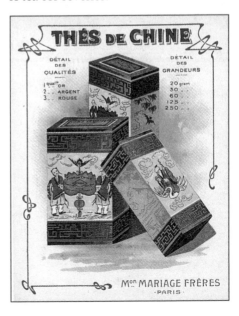

THÉS DE CHINE

DÉTAIL DES QUALITÉS
1 qualité OR
2 - ARGENT
3 - ROUGE

DÉTAIL DES GRANDEURS
20 gram
30 -
60 -
125 -
250 -

Mon MARIAGE FRÈRES
·PARIS·

• *Yellow China Tea*

*G*ROWN IN HUNAN PROVINCE, yellow tea is a most famous China tea. Plantations on Mount Jun have enjoyed great esteem for their subtle and refreshing teas since the days of the Tang dynasty.

The region produces both small-leaved yellow teas (such as Thé Jaune des Cinq Dynasties) and large-leaved teas (Huoshan, Liuan, and Yingshan).

Almost all yellow tea is consumed by Chinese amateurs. Only tiny quantities are exported.

T2212 THÉ JAUNE DES CINQ DYNASTIES
    'Five-Dynasty Yellow Tea' is one of the most costly teas in the world. Chinese emperors of the 'Five Dynasties' (907-960) received it as a sign of homage from their noble subjects.
This yellow tea is characterised by its elegant, golden buds.

Its subtly fragrant, brisk liquor has a smooth, slightly sweet taste.
Making this yellow tea provides unique entertainment for tea lovers. Stirred into a cup of 75°C (165°F) water, the leaves initially float, then begin an extraordinary ballet by sinking to the bottom and rising to the surface several times.
Then they slowly come to a halt, standing vertically like bamboo shoots, so that their graceful shape and golden yellow colour can be admired.
'Five-Dynasty Yellow Tea' is the rarest of teas, the most sought-after by true connoisseurs.
Absolute magic.

• Blue China Teas

*O*RIGINALLY FROM WU YI Mountain in Fujian Province, blue teas, generally called Oolong or Qing Cha, have been a great Chinese specialty since the days of the Song dynasty.
They were among the first teas to be known and appreciated in seventeenth-century Europe, after green tea but before black tea.
Although the main producing regions are in Fujian Province, some blue teas come from Guangdong.

'Bal Masqué' Teapot.

The Chinese claim that blue teas are the most beneficial for health, because they help to maintain a good metabolic balance by reducing fats and eliminating toxins from the body.
For hundreds of years, the Chinese have been drinking large quantities of blue tea daily.

T2310   ROBE ROUGE
'Red Gown', called Da Hong Pao on Wu Yi Mountain where it is grown, is extremely rare.
A tiny estate on a steep slope with sandy soil near a spring provides the tea bushes with morning sun but protects them with cool afternoon shade. The tender buds with red reflections thus benefit from ideal conditions, enhancing all their qualities.
Just after picking, leaves undergo a bold oxidation that releases a highly woody taste specific to the soil. Its thick, concentrated liquor and its grand aroma, halfway between chestnut and hazelnut, last long in the mouth.
A masterpiece envied by connoisseurs the world over, it has been valued since the Ming dynasty for allegedly favouring a long life.

T2311   TI KUAN YIN SUPRÊME
Lightly oxidised, Ti Kuan Yin Suprême is composed of specially selected, finely rolled dark green leaves. Its golden yellow liquor yields a silky cup with a highly delicate taste of white flowers that simultaneously produce the sappy freshness and woody spark of oolongs from China.

A perfect balance between the gentle fragrance of green teas and the delicate aroma of black teas.

T2312 TI KUAN YIN D'OR

This oolong is one of China's most famous teas. Smooth, sophisticated, and only partly oxidised (15%), it is composed solely of the youngest and tenderest leaves.
It features a grand, flowery fragrance and yields a golden liquor with jade highlights.
Its brilliant elixir, similar to a just-budding orchid, lasts long in the mouth. Pure silk for the palate.

T231 TI KUAN YIN
'Iron Goddess of Mercy'

Grown in Fujian Province, this tea has fine, dark leaves and a concentrated taste that remains long in the mouth.
A subtle, slightly flowery tea with delicate, local flavour.
Offering guests a cup of Ti Kuan Yin is a sign of respect.

T232 KWAI FLOWER

Known in China as 'peach tea', the large, open leaves of this tea are skilfully blended with pollen from flowers of the Chinese bay tree.
A brilliant cup, highly pleasant taste.
Appropriate for afternoon and evening.

T233 SHUI HSIEN
'Water Sprite'

Mild and slightly spicy, with a clear, sparkling liquor.
A daytime tea.

T234 SE CHUNG
'Little Leaf'

Similar to Ti Kuan Yin but gives a darker liquor and stronger taste.
An afternoon tea.

T235 FENGHUANG DANCONG

A masterpiece from Guangdong Province. Benefiting from a favourable climate, this famous tea features a grand floral nose, a golden liquor, and a sweet, intense flavour.
An evening tea par excellence.

T236 DUVET DU DRAGON

'Dragon Down' comes from the high mountains of Hunan Province. It is an oolong that has undergone fairly lengthy oxidation, and is composed of young, downy shoots that give off a marvellous flavour of sweet chestnuts. Highly original.

• *Black China Teas*

*B*LACK TEA WAS DEVELOPED IN China around the middle of the Ming Dynasty (14th–15th centuries). The oldest garden producing black tea is located in the Wu Yi Mountain district, in northern Fujian Province.

Europeans call it 'black tea', because the oxidation process turns the leaves a very dark colour.
The Chinese, meanwhile, call it 'red tea' due to the colour of the liquor. Black tea represents 25% of China's total output of tea, and 50% of its exports.
There are two major types of black China tea–plain and smoky.

Plain Black China Teas

Yunnan Province

These teas grown 'beneath the clouds' are reputed to be the 'kings of black China teas'.

The Camellia Assamica tea plant is grown on the high misty plateaus of southern China, not far from the town of Fengqing. Graced by an unusually favourable climate, black teas from Yunnan–called 'Dianhong'–are distinguished by fine, golden-tipped leaves and a unique taste that is dry, flowery, delicate, rich, spicy, and highly fragrant all at once.

T2023   AIGUILLES D'OR, SFTGFOP1
Treated like a white tea, these rare 'Golden Needles' are composed exclusively of gold tips, dried in the sun and oxidised naturally.
Produced in highly limited quantities, this tea is almost impossible to find.
Its round, malty flavour, strong and scented, recalls honey made from longan flowers. It lasts long in the mouth, exalting all its fragrances.
It is the Yin Zhen ('Silver Needles') of black teas.

T2000   YUNNAN D'OR, SFTGFOP1
This majestic 'Golden Yunnan' is truly cultivated 'beneath the clouds' in the red soil of the Lancang River, according to age-old methods.
Like Pu-Erh teas, it is known for its beneficial qualities. Its fine, elegant young leaves with their many golden tips produce a caramelized fragrance evocative of hazelnuts and spices.
A distinguished taste, finely balanced between strength and subtlety, remains long and deep in the mouth.
A highly sophisticated daytime tea.

T2001   ROI DU YUNNAN, FTGFOP1
A highly rare gem, this 'King of Yunnan' is the product of an extraordinarily careful plucking.
It is extremely rich in golden tips, and possesses substantial body.
Its grand aroma and smooth, flowery taste caress the palate.
A wonderful afternoon tea.

Sorting tea, China, 1900.

T200   YUNNAN IMPÉRIAL, TGFOP
A top quality harvest representing one of Yunnan's most reputable teas, thanks to its handsome leaves, numerous golden tips, dry taste, full flavour.
A truly grand breakfast tea.

T201   GRAND YUNNAN, TGFOP
This tea is characterized by its large leaves and numerous golden tips. Highly aromatic, with a flavour that fills the palate.
A good breakfast and daytime tea.

T202   YUNNAN, FOP
Large, golden-tipped leaves
identical to the Grand Yunnan above,
though with a smaller proportion of
golden tips.
An aroma and taste of honey.
A daytime tea.

Anhui Province
'A rose among beauties'.

Anhui Province, located to the west of
Shanghai, is one of the largest tea-
producing regions in China.
Thanks to a subtropical climate on
mountain gardens over 3,000 feet high
(notably on the famous slopes of
Huang Shan and Jihuan Shan), teas
from Anhui have enjoyed an excellent
reputation throughout the world for
centuries. Keemun, for instance,
known as 'tea from Lion Mountain',
has a subtle scent of orchids and a
brilliant red liquor with a mild, sweet
taste. The flavour is all the more
exquisite for being non-astringent.

Crafted Black China Tea

T2031   BOUQUET DE THÉ NOIR
This 'crafted' tea is an
extraordinary sculptural composition
from mysterious Huang Shan
Mountain.
Young, tender leaves are bound by
hand into a delicate bouquet of
exquisite fragrance.
One bouquet per person should be
steeped in a chung (or cup with cover)
for five minutes—yet another refined
way of appreciating tea.

Black China Leaf Teas

T2032   ROI DU KEEMUN, FTGFOP1
A highly rare black tea, the 'King
of Keemun' is a magnificent Gongfu–or
ceremonial–tea. The estate, hidden on a
misty mountain, enjoys nature's favours
in the form of abundant rain and mild
temperatures. The broad, handsome
leaves include many golden tips.
The liquor is bright red, the flavour mild
and sweet, while the aroma recalls the
scent of orchids. A sovereign tea.

Sifting tea, China, 1900.

T2030   KEEMUN IMPÉRIAL, FOP
This rare Keemun is one of the
most highly sought varieties. Its fine,
shiny leaves yield a subtle aroma and
delicate taste. The height of
refinement. The tea chosen by the
Court of Saint James when celebrating
the birthday of the Queen of England.

T203   GRAND KEEMUN, FOP
A great harvest of handsome
leaves, producing a highly aromatic,
mild, slightly flowery tea. A digestive
tea, low in theine. Appropriate for the
evening.

T204   KEEMUN, FOP
A light, mild, somewhat sweet
tea, perfect for afternoon and evening.

Szechwan Province

Heavenly Teas.

Szechwan Province pioneered the production of quality teas. Its gardens are located in the famous Meng Mountain district, nearly 5,000 feet high. Abundant rain and heavy mists create uniquely perfect conditions for growing this tea.

T2060 SZECHWAN IMPÉRIAL, TGFOP1
Grown at the top of Meng Mountain, this is the supreme Szechwan tea thanks to the bloom of its golden-tipped leaves with their intense yet refined nose.
The orangey-red liquor produces a flowery aroma and a subtly sweet flavour.
A truly grand evening tea.

T206 SZECHWAN, FOP
A high quality Szechwan tea featuring handsome, tippy leaves. Its dark liquor has a particularly flowery, round, and sustained aroma. An afternoon tea for connoisseurs.

Other Provinces

T2095 JIANGXI IMPÉRIAL, TGFOP1
Known in China as the 'King of Black Teas', this majestic Gongfu tea is one of the most subtle of black China teas. It is also highly prized, particularly by Russians. Grown in Jiang Xi Province in southeastern China, and plucked only in spring, it is not unlike Keemun Impérial in nature.
Its handsome leaves have many

golden tips. Its bright red liquor is succulently sweet, making it an excellent afternoon tea.

T205 NINGCHOW, FOP
A whole-leaf, tippy tea from Hu Bei Province, with a slightly flowery aroma. A mild tea to be drunk all day long.

Smoky Black China Teas

Fujian Province

Smoky teas were first developed in Chongan County in the seventeenth century.
According to Chinese legend, imperial army troops during the Qing Dynasty (1644–1912) passed through a small village and decided to bivouac in a tea manufactory full of freshly plucked leaves. The presence of the troops significantly delayed the processing of the fresh leaves, and the factory artisans feared they would miss their delivery deadline. So they decided to light fires of pine logs to accelerate the drying process. The now-famous pine smoke markedly flavoured the leaves–'Lapsang

Packing tea, China, 1900.

Souchong' had just been invented. Its name comes from the Chinese phrase Zhengshan xiaozhong, which means 'variety of tea from the veritable Wu Yi mountain'.

The Chinese smoke their tea in artisanal fashion.
After oxidation, Souchong leaves are grilled on a hot iron plate, then arranged on bamboo racks over a fire fuelled by green pine logs that give off their scent.
Smoky teas are known for their substantial character.

T210   LAPSANG SOUCHONG IMPÉRIAL
The most refined of smoky teas–its long, uniformly handsome leaves are carefully smoked over rare wood in a traditional manner. A rich yet subtle tea for daytime.

T211   GRAND LAPSANG SOUCHONG
High quality, large whole leaves, smoked in traditional manner and impregnated with the smell of the famous Chinese pine roots. Clear and full flavoured. Excellent with savoury and spicy dishes.

T212   LAPSANG SOUCHONG
A moderately smoky, fine whole-leaf Lapsang.

T213   TARRY SOUCHONG
A highly smoky, fine whole-leaf Lapsang.

• *Matured China Teas*

GROWN AT AN ALTITUDE of 3,000 to 4,000 feet, along the Lancong River in Xishuanbanna, south-western Yunnan Province, these black teas benefit not only from a perfect climate - between 15° and 20°C (60°/72°F) all year round - but also from the rich, fertile soil of this misty, hilly region.

Preparing tea chests, China, 1900.

T2020 PU-ERH D'OR

This 'gold' Pu-Erh was the authentic, precious tea of Chinese tribes under the Song and Qing dynasties. Only the young buds are chosen, carefully plucked early in the year (February), before the rainy season starts, when they are still fine and covered with down. With its elegant, golden leaves, this rare Pu-Erh is never packaged as a compressed tea. Its liquor is deep red, dense yet mild with a scent of lotus and a slightly sweet taste. Aromatic and aged, it represents the height of refinement. It also boasts beneficial and soothing qualities.

T2021 PU-ERH

Known in the Far East for its medicinal properties, and designed to be compressed into cakes of tea, Pu-Erh has a completely unique taste. It gives a deep red liquor that fills the palate with a pleasantly earthy, slightly sugary taste. A highly beneficial beverage.

T2022 PU-ERH D'OUTRE-MER

This 'overseas' Pu-Erh is highly prized by Chinese emigrants abroad; sprinkled with chrysanthemum flowers, it is known in Canton tea houses as Gook Po Cha. Its taste evokes a mossy, flowery copse, transporting the palate to distant lands drenched in fine rain. It is well-known for its refreshing, soothing qualities.

T2024 PU-ERH FLEUR DE THÉ

For the first time ever, MARIAGE FRÈRES has combined a red-coloured Pu-Erh grown on the high misty plateaus of Yunnan, referred to as the land of eternal spring, with the flowers of Camellia

Sinensis. The dense and sustained aroma of mossy earth and tea tree bark, together with the intense fragrances of the soil, merge with the fresh and fine wildflower scent. It creates a striking and original contrast in grain and finesse and yields a liquor that invades the palate and gives lasting aftertaste pleasure. A magnificent after meal tea.

• Compressed China Teas

*T*HE FIRST SCHOOL OF TEA –'boiled tea'– emerged during the reign of the powerful, brilliant Tang dynasty (618–907). The weeks just after harvesting were devoted to the manufacture of tea. In order to produce bricks or cakes of tea, the leaves were first crushed–releasing their flavour–then pressed into molds. Wrapped and bound, the bricks were then transported in baskets dangling from the two ends of a pole, thereby reaching all the subjects of the Great Chinese Empire.

This method of drinking tea is still common in Tibet and among various Mongol tribes.

T240 BRIQUE DE THÉ, PU-ERH DU YUNNAN VINTAGE 1999

This compressed square 'brick' of large, shiny tea leaves comes from the misty slopes of Yunnan's mountains. Notably known for its refreshing, energising, beneficial properties, this tea has the unusual feature of improving with age. The 1999 vintage is stamped with the Chinese ideograms for good luck: a vestige of the 20th century, a gift for the 21st.

T241   BRIQUE DE THÉ, DSCHUAN CHA

This 'Brick of Tea', compressed into a traditional shape (9.5 in x 7.5 in x 1 in, 2.5 pounds) and decorated with legendary patterns, is produced by the famous Zhao Li Qiao manufactory in Hu Bei Province. Song dynasty emperors decided that taxes would be paid in the form of bricks of tea. The tea can obviously be drunk, but the brick also serves as a fine decorative item, making a fragrant, poetic gift.

T2410   BRIQUE DE THÉ VERT

A fine green tea is compressed into a 'brick' of rare rectangular shape (7.4 in x 4.7 in x 0.8 in, approx. 0.9 pounds). The ideograms covering it recall the decoration of La Porte Chinoise, a famous oriental boutique that opened in Paris in 1862. A perfect gift signifying friendship and happiness.

T243   NATTE DE THÉ MÉDICINAL

This is a 'braid' of five balls of tea from Guangdong Province. Each ball yields a litre of deliciously refreshing tea with digestive, fever-suppressing virtues. Two braids in a hot tub produce a relaxing, healthy bath.

T244   TUO CHA

This matured tea from Yunnan Province, with its slightly earthy taste, is pressed into the shape of a 'bird's nest'. It enjoys a solid reputation, and when drunk regularly can help lower the level of triglycerides in the blood.

T2440   TUO CHA LUBAO

A famous, traditional green tea, also from Yunnan Province, pressed into the form of a tiny bird's nest. It enjoys the same worldwide reputation as its companion, Tuo Cha. Each tiny bird's nest produces a mild, refined, relaxing taste.

FORMOSA

Some 200 years ago, tea plants from Fujian Province on mainland China were first planted on the northern part of the island of Formosa.

THANKS TO DIVINE WEATHER – the temperature never rises above 28°C (82°F) in summer yet never drops below 13°C (55°F) in winter – tea gardens developed wonderfully on Formosa. The island's great specialty is blue teas.

• Blue Formosa Teas
Chinese Method

T2710   TUNG TING JADE

This marvel from Tung Ting is an elegant Formosa Oolong. It is highly appreciated by connoisseurs the world over. Its handsome, carefully processed leaves and its brilliant liquor both recall the rich colour of jade. This noble tea yields a flowery, fragrant cup.

T2701 TUNG TING

Grown on Tung Ting Mountain, this tea is reputed to be one of the finest from Formosa.
It is very slightly oxidised, producing an orangey-red liquor and a mild flavour.
A tea for festive occasions.

T2702 GRAND POUCHONG IMPÉRIAL

Tung Ting's great rival.
The finest Grand Pouchong leaves are just slightly oxidised, yielding a liquor with fine golden colour and delicate aroma.
A daytime tea.

Harvesting tea, Formosa, 1910.

T2703 TI KUAN YIN IMPÉRIAL

Known for its beneficial qualities, this partly oxidised tea has an amber liquor with highly developed aroma and mild flavour.
A digestive tea.

Formosan Method: 'Oriental Beauty'

Like China, Formosa produces black, green, and flavoured teas as well as the most famous of blue teas, Oolong (which literally means 'Black Dragon').

According to legend, a planter was plucking tea leaves in his garden in Fujian Province on mainland China when he suddenly detected an extraordinary fragrance coming from one of his tea plants.
He headed toward the bush and discovered a magnificent black serpent coiled around the plant. Interpreting this as a lucky omen, the man immediately plucked some leaves and made tea from them. To his great joy, he discovered a new, sublime flavour that no other beverage had yet produced. This tea plant has subsequently be cultivated under the name 'Black Dragon'.

T2700 ORIENTAL BEAUTY

The height of perfection among Formosa Oolong teas. The rarest, most subtle, most distinguished and most highly appreciated Formosa Oolong has been dubbed 'Oriental Beauty' by true connoisseurs.
It is grown in the hills of the famous province of Tao Yuan on northern Formosa.
The harvest, which takes place in June, is considered to be the finest of the year. The plucking of the youngest leaves is scrupulously done by hand.
Planters are careful to process the tea according to age-old methods.
The long, elegant leaves with their numerous white tips produce a grand fragrance evocative of wild orchids.
Oriental Beauty should be steeped for

Gelée Extra de Thé

TARRY SOUCHONG

5 minutes, using pure, simmering water–this will release its incomparably delicate flavour, with a marked flowery note filling the palate.

A prestigious tea for those precious moments. Strongly recommended as an accompaniment for caviar.

T270   OOLONG IMPÉRIAL
A gem among gems. This fine, rare tea has a golden liquor, flowery aroma, and subtle flavour.
Divine.

T271   GRAND OOLONG FANCY
'Grand Black Dragon'
An exceptional, spring plucking selects only handsome whole leaves with silver tips. Terrific aroma, exquisite taste, great sophistication. A refined tea for important celebrations–true splendour.

T272   OOLONG FANCY
This summer harvest is known for its outstanding bouquet.
The handsome whole leaves produce a flowery aroma and bright liquor. Most appropriate for late afternoon and evening.

T273   GRAND OOLONG
A romantic, highly fragrant tea with extremely pleasant flavour and limpid liquor. Suitable for pleasant, relaxing occasions.

T274   OOLONG
Subtle, mild, aromatic, pleasant. Recommended for late afternoon and evening.

• *Smoky Black Formosa Tea*

T251   TARRY SOUCHONG
A large-leaf tea impregnated with smoke from special, rare Formosan woods. Heavily smoked, giving a special aroma and flavour. Highly appreciated by connoisseurs of smoky teas. Excellent accompaniment to English-style breakfasts.

• *Green Formosa Tea*

T2617   GUNPOWDER ZHU CHA
Leaves rolled into little balls. Delicious on its own, but also prized as the basis of North African mint tea when fresh mint leaves are added. Most refreshing.

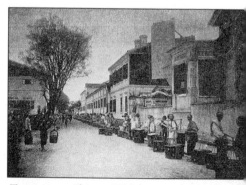

Tea porters, China, 1900.

INDIA

The main tea-growing regions of India are found in the Himalaya foothills in the northeast, the Assam valley to the east, and the Nilgiri mountain region in the south.

India has become the world's leading producer of tea, and the number four exporter.

Darjeeling

'Tea of Mountain Mists'
Darjeeling, without a doubt the most refined, noble, and precious Indian tea, is sometimes called 'the champagne of black teas'.

THUS THE MOST FAMOUS TEA IN the world is named after a modest Indian town.

The plantations around Darjeeling are situated at altitudes ranging from 3,000 to 7,000 feet, on the southern slopes of the immense Himalaya range between Bhutan, Nepal, and Sikkim.

This lofty altitude, along with cool temperatures, moist climate, ample sunshine, and exceptionally good soil, endows the tea leaves with a rich aroma, an exquisite bouquet, and a particularly subtle flavour (reminiscent of muscatel grapes, almonds, and ripe fruit).

Darjeeling boasts 87 estates, the most famous of which are Castleton, Jungpana, Margaret's Hope, Namring, Lingia, Seeyok, Risheehat, and Bannockburn. All of these estates produce outstanding teas, proving the adage that they are to Indian tea what champagne is to French wine.

Yet the special prestige of Darjeeling teas also stems from their abundant variety and multiple charms.

Above all, however, the production of Darjeeling tea is still an art, allowing experts to display the full range of their craft.

For example, while some stages of production can now be mechanized, oxidation must still be done 'by the nose'. During the brief oxidation process, the planter must pay constant attention to the precise moment when the process should be halted in order to obtain the finest results; this entails examining and smelling the leaf, assessing the exact point at which oxidation will yield the liveliest aroma and brightest liquor.

The ultimate goal of all of these operations is nothing less than total excellence.

Tea estate, Darjeeling, 1920.

Not only does each estate have its own personality, but even within an estate none of the many batches of a given harvest is identical to any other. The Mariage Frères taster is therefore obliged to make a selection from among dozens of Darjeeling teas from a single estate (say, Castleton) and a single picking (first flush, for example). Just as quality varies, so does price. Specialists therefore refrain from making comparisons based solely on the name of the estate.

• Black Darjeeling Teas

First Flush: Spring Harvest

In general, plucking is done between late February and mid April, but cold weather may affect the exact date.
Characteristics: The dry leaves of first flush teas have a brownish green colour, and a high proportion of tips. Once steeped, they turn quite green and give off an intense, unique fragrance. The liquor is a very bright golden yellow colour. It is recommended that the dose of first flush teas be increased from 2.5 g to 3.5 g per cup, and that steeping time be reduced to 2 or 3 minutes.

The spring harvest produces young, highly aromatic teas with a remarkably flowery, light, and refined taste recalling muscatel grapes or green almonds.

These 'early' teas are wonderfully refreshing. A rare treat.

T100   CASTLETON, SFTGFOP1
One of the oldest and most esteemed estates in Darjeeling, situated at an altitude of 5,200 feet, near Kurseong. Early spring's finest yield. Perfect appearance, sublime fragrance, exquisite taste of young muscatel. The height of refinement.

T1000   BLOOMFIELD, SFTGFOP1
A sentimental favourite, Bloomfield boasts fabulous harvests. Very fine leaves with silvery tips, thoroughly typical of first flush. A magnificent tea for the afternoon.

T1001   LINGIA, SFTGFOP1
At an altitude of 6,500 feet, Lingia is one of the most beautiful estates, and produces a most handsome tea. Pale golden liquor, slightly sweet cup with a subtle hint of exotic flowers. An excellent tea for those special moments.

The Most Prestigious Estates in Darjeeling

T1002 AMBOOTIA, FTGFOP1
Outstanding quality, very fine leaves with noble nose, brilliant liquor, mild yet slightly spicy taste. A great tea all day long.

T1003 MAKAIBARI, FTGFOP1
Located to the south of Kurseong at an altitude of 4,500 feet, the Makaibari estate enjoys an excellent reputation in France.
Its famous tea has the lively, refined taste of green almonds. Extremely direct, wonderful in the afternoon.

T1005 NAMRING UPPER, SFTGFOP1
An excellent harvest from a magnificent estate some 7,000 feet high, yielding one of the finest bouquets of all first flush Darjeelings. The Namring estate sacrificed part of its autumnal harvest by cutting its plants back in July, in order to prepare them for a very early spring plucking.
The result is positively exquisite–the tea blossoms in the mouth, developing a distinguished flavour of green almonds. The cup is luminous, flowery, sweet. A regal afternoon tea.

T1006 THURBO, FTGFOP1
One of the prides of the spring harvest. According to legend, the name Thurbo derives from 'Tombu', a word for the tents used by the British army during its Nepalese campaign. Located in the picturesque Mirik district, the Thurbo estate produces a first flush tea of extraordinary quality. Its fine, carefully worked leaves yield intense flavours

and a bright, heady liquor with fine, flowery bouquet. A grand tea for the afternoon.

T1008 JUNGPANA SFTGFOP1
One of Darjeeling's treasures, Jungpana means 'gentle young lady' in Tibetan. Indeed, the estate is one of the most glamorous tea gardens in Darjeeling, nestling at an altitude of over 7,000 feet northeast of Darjeeling Town.
This brilliant harvest constitutes a magnificent spring bouquet: its fine, elegant leaves yield a sweet, flowery pale green liquor accompanied by a grandly intense yet harmonious fragrance. A stunning afternoon tea.

T101 MARGARET'S HOPE, SFTGFOP1
A divinely majestic tea from an estate near the town of Darjeeling (4,800 feet), which is highly renowned for the quality of its spring and summer harvests. Its refined, aromatic bouquet and delicate flavour delights sophisticated palates. Bright, crystalline liquor.True splendour.

T1010 ARYA, FTGFOP1
This small estate, highly prized by Japanese connoisseurs, is situated above Darjeeling at an elevation of 6,000 feet. In order to produce this rare tea of wonderful quality, only the most tender, pale green leaves are picked, at an interval of every three days rather than the usual once a week. Noted for its subtle aroma, elegant leaves, and smooth liquor, this is a tea of great polish, appropriate at any time of the day.

T102   SOOM, FTGFOP1

Located in northwestern Darjeeling, near Sikkim, at an altitude of 5,200 feet, this estate is famous for the exceptional quality of its first flush tea, characterized by its uniform leaves, fresh scent, and mild taste of green almonds.
An admirable afternoon choice.

T103   TUMSONG, FTGFOP1

This tiny estate, perched 4,500 feet up a slope near the Nepalese border, almost exclusively produces teas grown from Chinese plants. Beautiful, tippy leaves yield a flavorful, flowery taste and bright, airy liquor. A succulent afternoon tea.

T104   PUTTABONG, FTGFOP1

Puttabong, nestling near the Sikkim border at an altitude of 5,200 feet, is one of Darjeeling's most prestigious estates. This tea displays all the characteristics of a first flush Darjeeling: its fine leaves are carefully rolled, its flavour is mild and light, its aroma sublime. An afternoon splendour.

T105   GIELLE, FTGFOP1

A marvellous estate near the Teesta River, at an elevation of 5,200 feet, producing equally reputable first and second flushes. All the freshness of spring, with an exquisite flavour appreciated by the most refined palates. An appropriate tea for brunch.

T106   OAKS, FTGFOP1

In the middle of Darjeeling, near Ghum (one of the highest train stations in the world), this 5,200-foot high estate boasts marvellous first flush teas grown exclusively from Chinese plants. A dazzling liquor, smooth in taste, that recalls young muscatel.
A rich afternoon tea.

T107   SINGTOM, FTGFOP

A leading first flush, with a flowery note that appeals to French tastes. Pale golden liquor.
A delicate tea for any time of day.

T108   SPRINGSIDE, FTGFOP

A great harvest from an estate near Castleton, with full leaves famous for their balanced taste. Highly refined and aromatic, with a fine, mild liquor. Perfect for tea breaks.

T109   ORANGE VALLEY, TGFOP

Grand quality from the Bloomfield domain. Tippy leaves, of moderate size, yielding a limpid, bright, flowery cup. A daytime tea.

T110   NAMRING, TGBOP

This broken-leaf tea, from a grand estate, gives a full-bodied, aromatic liquor. A rich, morning tea that can take a drop of cold milk.

Tea factory, 1900.

T1100 LINGIA, BPS

A flowery bouquet from a charming estate to the west of Darjeeling, ranging from 4,500 to 5,800 feet in altitude. Combines the strength of fine, broken Pekoe Souchong leaves with the fragrance of first flush Darjeelings. An ideal tea to accompany a continental breakfast.

Porters with chests of Darjeeling tea, 1900.

Second Flush: Summer Harvest

The summer plucking, which takes place between May and June, is the largest harvest of the year.

It produces teas of excellent quality.

Characteristics: Leaves are dark brown, with many silver tips. Once steeped, the leaves become coppery and highly aromatic. The liquor is a fine, dark gold.

Second flush teas have a grand yet delicate aroma, and a remarkably ripe, fruity taste. Their round, lively flavour is somewhat stronger than first flush teas.

T1109 BRUMES D'HIMALAYA, SFTGFOP1

'Himalayan Mists', created specially for MARIAGE FRÈRES, is a highly prestigious black tea produced on the renowned Ambootia Estate in the misty mountains of Darjeeling. Like white teas, it is composed solely of silvery buds.

The extremely selective plucking occurs only in the coolness of an evening under a rising moon.

A delicate withering happens during the night; then the leaves are gently rolled at dawn (each bud having already been wrapped in a larger leaf for protection). The young, downy leaves produce a golden liquor tasting of hazelnut and muscatel, with a unique, unforgettable floral aroma.

T1110 CASTLETON, SFTGFOP1

The famous Castleton estate produces the king of summer Darjeelings, regularly breaking sales records at the Calcutta auction.

Its sculpted, tippy leaves produce a chestnut-coloured liquor.

Castleton is known for its distinctive taste of muscatel and a special aroma which is simultaneously intense and subtle. The most glamorous and precious of Indian teas. Grandiose.

T1111 JUNGPANA, SFTGFOP1

Castleton's great rival is known for its imperial dignity. The famous Jungpana estate regularly breaks its own sales record at the Calcutta auction. Located at an altitude of over 4,000 feet, to the southeast of Darjeeling Town, Jungpana produces a typical second flush with its own fruity taste of hazelnuts. A magnificent tea for special occasions.

T1112 SELIMBONG, FTGFOP1

This glorious estate on the high Himalaya plateaus is noted for its fine, chestnut leaves with numerous silver tips. Its round, full flavour is backed by an intense aroma. The golden liquor has a pronounced fruity taste. A glamorous daytime tea.

T112 NAMRING UPPER, SFTGFOP1

'The valley of sunny dawns'

An excellent high-grown tea from an estate located at an altitude of over 7,000 feet. The first seeds, brought from China by the British, were planted here as early as 1855. Namring boasts one of the finest bouquets among second flushes. Its fine leaves produce a well-balanced, fruity taste that dazzles the palate. For grand occasions.

T1120 AMBOOTIA, SFTGFOP1

An exceptional harvest characterized by highly colourful leaves. A subtle, fruity hint of black currant makes this a most grand, refined beverage for the afternoon.

T113 PUTTABONG, FTGFOP1

One of the largest estates in Darjeeling, Puttabong is known for its great second flush–highly aromatic, with a strong note of fresh peach. Full in the mouth, it is an ideal afternoon tea.

T114 RISHEEHAT, FTGFOP1

A well-known garden to the east of Darjeeling Town, at an altitude of 4,500 feet. Its finely rolled leaves are the product of an outstanding harvest.

'Théière des Légendes.'

Its noble aroma is refinement itself, yielding a fragrant cup without the least trace of bitterness. A daytime tea.

T115 GOOMTEE, FTGFOP1

Goomtee, situated at 6,500 feet in the Kurseong district to the east of Darjeeling, produces a prestigious second flush. It is known for its outstanding quality and famous taste of hazelnuts. A 'tea of mountain mists' that goes wonderfully well with refined food.

T116 MARGARET'S HOPE, FTGFOP

A British favourite–highly aromatic, harvested at just the right moment in summer. Its round, full flavour is perfect for the morning.

T117 SINGBULLI, TGFOP

Excellent quality from a grand estate located in the Mirik district to the south, at an altitude of 3,900 feet. This tea produces a smooth yet lively cup with a hint of muscatel. A fine afternoon choice.

T118 GIELLE, FTGFOP

A tea with great character, thanks to careful handling of its fine, chestnut-coloured leaves with silver tips. Its luminous, aromatic liquor has a full, round taste with a note reminiscent of black currants. A refined breakfast tea.

T1180 CHAMONG, FTGFOP1

A sentimental favourite at MARIAGE FRÈRES, Chamong is a well-known estate in Rungbong district, near Nepal. Situated at 4,500 feet, the leaves of this high-grown tea are often twisted, giving a full-bodied cup with fruity, fragrant flavour. French-style tea par excellence.

T1181 LINGIA, FTGFOP1

A handsome tea from a handsome, carefully maintained estate. Its attractive leaves produce a golden, lively liquor with substantial body. A poetic tea.

T1182 BANNOCKBURN, FTGFOP1

Founded in 1860, this estate is known for its reliable quality. Its fine leaves, full aroma, and developed flavour (with an aftertaste of raisins) make it a perfect tea for brunch.

T1183 PHOOBSERING, FTGFOP1

A fine tea whose uniformly handsome leaves yield an amber liquor with powerful aroma and almond-like flavour. An afternoon tea.

T119 TEESTA VALLEY, TGFOP

This distinguished estate is located near the Teesta River, on the edge of Gielle, at some 4,500 feet. It is known for its high proportion of Chinese plants. The tea is golden in colour, with a round, markedly aromatic taste. Suitable for brunch.

T120 POOBONG, FTGFOP

A highly appreciated harvest from a well-known estate to the west of Ghum. This typical second flush has a distinct taste of muscatel, similar to Namring. A perfect choice for five o'clock tea.

T121 SUNGMA, FTGFOP1

A revered summer tea produced by a charming estate at an altitude of 4,500 feet. Its fine leaves produce a bright, flavorful liquor whose smooth taste is reminiscent of muscatel. A grand afternoon tea.

T122 SELIM HILL, FTGFOP1

One of the vastest estates in Darjeeling, Selim Hill nevertheless produces high quality second flushes. It is located at an altitude of 4,500 feet in the Kurseong district. Its distinctly fruity cup is pleasantly round in the mouth. Delightful at five o'clock.

'Opium' Teapot
Designed by MARIAGE FRÈRES, 1994.

T123 BALASUN, TGFOP

A famous estate to the south of Darjeeling Town, perched a mile high. Its white-tipped leaves yield a golden liquor and fully developed taste. A daytime tea.

T124 MOONDAKOTEE, BPS

A 'champion' second flush from an estate near Mirik, to the west of Darjeeling Town. Its Broken Pekoe Souchong leaves produce a full-bodied, lightly aromatic tea that is perfect for breakfast.

T125   MARGARET'S HOPE, TGBOP1
Broken leaves are designed to produce a powerful, rich cup that is round in the mouth.
A grand breakfast tea, it can take a drop of milk.

Monsoon Flush

This harvest takes place during the romantic monsoon season in August and September.
The liquor is deeper in colour and more pronounced in taste.

T1250   KALEJ VALLEY, FTGFOP1
A monsoon tea from a famous estate located south of Ghoom, near the Silguri railway line, at an altitude of 6,400 feet.
Large, regular leaves produce an amber liquor graced by a sent of muscatel grapes.
Perfect for a continental breakfast.

Autumn Flush

The autumn plucking, which takes place from October to November, produces high quality teas.
The dark brown leaves yield a coppery liquor.

T1260   ARYA 'ROSE D'HIMALAYA', SFTGFOP1
One of Darjeeling's mysteries, this rare autumnal tea boasts a unique, unexplained feature–its elegant leaves and red liquor evoke the suave fragrance of roses. The succulent cup carries a hint not only of rosebuds but also of ripe fruit.Magic.

T126   MARGARET'S HOPE, FTGFOP1
An early autumnal tea, with full aroma, round taste, and substantial body. A good daytime tea.

The Art of Darjeeling Blends

Blends of the finest harvests, whether from different estates or from different pluckings, offer unique flavours and guarantee reliable quality.

T1270   DARJEELING IMPÉRIAL, SFTGFOP1
A noble blend, marrying the heady bouquet of spring to summer's sweet note of ripe fruit.
A dazzling tea for special occasions

T127   QUEEN VICTORIA, FTGFOP
The outstanding quality of this blend–second flushes from the finest estates–makes it a must. A refined, fragrant tea for the morning, preferably without milk.

T128   MASTER, TGFOP
A great blend of first flush, second flush, and autumnal harvests. Its rich aroma and balanced taste make it a fine tea all day long.

T129   PRINCETON, TGFOP
An extremely refined and subtle blend of first flush teas from various estates. A brisk, flowery tea of incomparable flavour. Perfect for five o'clock tea.

T130   RAJAH, TGFOP
A quality blend of second flush teas, yielding a frank, richly coloured tea. Ideal for an afternoon break.

• Green Darjeeling Tea

T141   ARYA

This unoxidised Darjeeling, from the prestigious Arya estate, is a great rarity. The sublime savour of this excellent green tea makes it a romantic drink.

• White Darjeeling Teas

T143   AMBOOTIA 'HIMALAYA PEONY'

A magnificent white Darjeeling. Produced in the same spirit as white Pai Mu Tan from China's Fujian Province, this rare tea combines the famous almond overtones of Darjeelings with the wildflower scent typical of white teas. Its handsome, curly leaves yield a luminous liquor and velvety taste.

T144   NEIGE DE JADE

"Jade Snow" was conceived like a precious work of art on the Arya estate in Darjeeling. It is a unique white tea from the land of the finest black teas – the leaves, plucked at dawn, are carefully spread in the sweet morning air, then each leaf is wrapped in silk cloth and rolled by hand, and finally placed in gentle sunlight. The crystalline liquor yields a refined taste of young growth with overtones of white flowers. The subtle fragrances of this grand tea last long in the mouth, whispering of rare pleasures.

• Blue Darjeeling Teas

T145   NAMRING DARJEELING OOLONG IMPÉRIAL

Prompted by MARIAGE FRÈRES, the famous Namring estate in Darjeeling developed a unique, Formosa-style Oolong tea. Its leaves are the product of the summer harvest, and merit the highest praise–broad and elegant, they have a fragrance of wild orchid and a subtle taste recalling both muscatel and chestnut. This magical tea ranks with the finest.

T146   BALASUN DARJEELING OOLONG FANCY

A treasure offered by a fine estate. Produced from the autumnal harvest, this Formosa-style

DARJEELING
OOLONG IMPÉRIAL

MARIAGE FRÈRES

Oolong retains its Darjeeling personality. Its amber liquor combines the taste of almond with a hint of chestnut. The flavoury, highly fragrant and slightly sweet cup makes a grand afternoon tea.

T147   FLEUR DE DARJEELING
    The mysterious, delicate alchemy of 'Darjeeling Flower' was concocted during a meeting on the high Himalayan plateaus between MARIAGE FRÈRES' taster and the Ambootia plantation owner. They found a perfect balance between the leaves and flowers of the tea bush, enabling the two to merge their fragrances. 'Darjeeling Flower' is built on an outstanding, blue tea with a mild flavour of honey, gold like pollen, to which the white flowers lend added fragrance. Very fresh in the mouth, a truly rare tea.

Assam

A SSAM, THE LARGEST TEA-producing region in the world, is located on the banks of the Brahmaputra River in northeastern India. In 1823, Robert Bruce

discovered wild tea bushes there. By 1834, British planters were setting up the first estates, of which there are some 2,000 today.

Assam teas come from a special variety of the plant, Camellia Assamica, that produces large, broad leaves. The often tippy teas feature a brilliant, deep red liquor and a particularly pronounced aroma. The powerful, round, full-bodied flavour carries a hint of spiciness. Assam teas happily take a drop of cold milk.

• *Black Assam Teas*

First Flush

In Assam, the first flush plucking is done between April and mid May. The resulting tea is marked by its freshness, clear liquor,

COOLIES. ASSAM.

and light cup. The finest first flush Assams are not unlike good Terai and Dooars teas harvested during the same period. First flush Assams are known only to connoisseurs, and therefore rarely sold in Europe.

T153   BAMONPOOKRI, TGFOP
    A top quality first flush tea. Its uniform, carefully processed leaves are greenish brown like those from Darjeeling. A strong yet refined breakfast tea.

T1531 NONAIPARA, TGFOP
A fine, early-plucked tea with broad leaves, giving a highly fragrant cup with a slight hint of spices. A daytime tea.

Second Flush

Second flush Assams are harvested between mid May and late June. They are characterized by handsome golden leaves giving a dark, full-bodied liquor that often has a malty taste. These are the teas favoured by the British.

T150 NUMALIGHUR, FTGFOP1
An excellent harvest from a grand estate, notable for its high proportion of golden tips. Plucked at just the right moment, it has a malty, spicy flavour and terrific aroma. A golden, daytime tea.

T151 NAPUK, FTGFOP1
This famous estate has produced a tea renowned for its grand aroma and balanced flavour. A morning tea par excellence.

T152 RUNGAGORA, FTGFOP
A top quality, tippy tea–savoury, yet with much finesse. A daytime tea.

T154 THOWRA, TGFOP
An outstanding second flush with frankly spicy taste. Its fine leaves boast many golden tips. A morning beverage.

T155 HARMUTTY, TGFOP
Full of body and strength, for a straightforward cup of tea. Highly aromatic, it can be drunk throughout the day.

T156 SILONIBARI, TGFOP
A well-known estate producing large-leaved tea with a strong, ample flavour that fills the palate. Perfect for brunch.

T157 MELENG, FOP
A rich and powerful tea from large leaves. For the morning.

T158 TARA, FOP
Characterized by long leaves that produce an equally long, fragrant taste. An afternoon choice.

T159 JAMIRAH, GFBOP
A tippy, broken-leaf tea with a strong, malty flavour that deliciously accompanies toast and marmalade.

T160 BETJAN, GFBOP
A full-bodied tea with rich aroma and malty flavour. A good choice for breakfast.

T161 MAUD, FBOP
A fine harvest yielding a very full-bodied tea with dark liquor. For the morning.

T162 SANKAR, BOP
A rich, second flush tea with body and strength. An excellent substitute for coffee, on rising in the morning.

• Green Assam Tea

T1620 KHONGEA
An unusual harvest, with a flowery nose. The young, dark buds produce a very clear, golden liquor with deliciously sweet taste. A most relaxing beverage.

Arunachal Pradesh

This mysterious region, at an average altitude of 1,600 feet above sea-level, is located between Assam and Bhutan. Teas from Arunachal Pradesh are extremely rare, for only one estate exists in the area.

T175   DONYI POLO, FTGFOP1
A real treasure–a grand tea with fawn-coloured leaves rich in tips. This gem combines the refinement of Darjeeling teas with the strength of Assams. Its brilliant red liquor is slightly lighter than Assam, yet highly aromatic. Its long fragrance fills the palate. A rare tea, for special days.

Dooars

This tiny Indian province to the west of Assam produces low-grown teas.

T181   GOOD HOPE, TGFOP
A great estate whose whole-leaf, first flush tea is less strong than Assam. Its cognac-coloured liquor is fresh, flowery, aromatic. A refined tea suitable for morning or afternoon.

Terai

Terai produces teas grown on the plain to the south of Darjeeling.

T171   ORD, TGFOP
A whole-leaf tea plucked at just the right moment. Its fine liquor has a strong flavour making it perfect for the morning.

Travancore

Travancore is a plateau region in southwestern India, of roughly the same altitude as the estates in Ceylon. Its teas are halfway between those grown in north India and those produced in Ceylon.

T191   HIGHGROWN, FBOP
The largest estate in south India offers a broken-leaf tea with a pronounced native tang. A fine tea on awakening.

Nilgiri

Nilgiri, or 'Blue Mountain', is located in southwestern India, and is a major tea-producing region. The best teas are harvested between January and March, when the monsoons to the northeast irrigate plains and plateaux. Top quality Nilgiri teas have much in common with good Ceylon varieties.

T192   NUNSUCH, TGFOP
A whole-leaf tea from the high plateaus of Blue Mountain. Its fruity aroma and lively, refined flavour is delightful all day long.

CEYLON

Ceylon teas are grown on estates in the mountainous region of the island of Sri Lanka, at altitudes ranging from 2,000 to 8,000 feet. Pure, healthy air and brilliant sunshine give these regal teas their famous aroma and beautiful golden colour.

'The Isle of Tea'

Ceylon is the world's leading exporter and third-ranked producer of tea. Ceylon teas are generally classified according to the altitude at which they are grown:

● *HIGH GROWN :*
Teas grown at the loftiest altitudes, from 4,000 to 8,000 feet. They are highly appreciated for their bright golden, fragrant liquor.

● *MIDDLE GROWN :*
Teas grown at average altitudes, between 2,000 and 4,000 feet. They are rich and smooth, with a handsome hue.

● *LOW GROWN :*
Teas grown at around 2,000 feet. Their liquor is dark and strong.
In recent years, however, the quality of Ceylon teas has slipped; their appearance, notably, has suffered from lack of quality control. It is increasingly difficult to find tea leaves that are clean, uniform, well-processed, and free of twigs. That is why MARIAGE FRÈRES pays special attention to its selection of local teas–only those of guaranteed quality are offered to our customers.

There are six main tea growing regions on the island:
● *KANDY* - the lower altitudes,
● *NUWARA ELIYA* - the highest region in the country,
● *DIMBULA* - to the west of the central mountain region,
● *UVA* - to the east of Dimbula,
● *RATNAPURA* - some 50 miles east of Colombo, the capital of Sri Lanka,
● *GALLE* - on the southern part of the island.

Each region produces a tea with its own specific flavour. All happily take a drop of cold milk.

● Black Ceylon Teas

Nuwara Eliya

Teas are grown in Nuwara Eliya, the highest region in Sri Lanka, all year round, and are reputed to be the 'Champagne of Ceylon teas'. Their light, brilliant liquor has a delicate, highly scented flavour.

T306   NUWARA ELIYA, OP
Ceylon's 'champagne'–light, brilliant, refined. An excellent afternoon tea.

THÉ
SUR LE
NIL

T3211 MAHA GASTOTTE, BOP
Grown on one of the most beautiful estates in Nuwara Eliya, this tea yields a light amber liquor of great freshness.
Its fully developed flavour is ideal for a continental breakfast.

T3181 TOMMAGONG, BOPF
This tea, from a well-known estate, is famous for its grand yet delicate aroma, its pronounced flavour, and its golden liquor.
A wake-up brew.

T324 LOVER'S LEAP, PEKOE
A romantic tea–its light golden liquor has a fragrant aroma that carries a hint of wild flowers.
Perfect for the morning.

Dimbula

This region is located to the west of the central mountain range, at an average altitude of 4,000 feet.

From December to March, the northeast monsoon unleashes heavy rains on the east coast even as the dry, cool climate on the west coast gives Dimbula teas their outstanding quality, characterized by a powerful aroma and a particularly rich body.

T302 PETTIAGALLA, OP1
An outstanding harvest from this very large estate in Balangoda district, to the south of Dimbula. Its long, fine leaves produce a highly aromatic tea with remarkably fruity taste.
This renowned Orange Pekoe is perfect for five o'clock tea.

T303 KENILWORTH, OP1
Plucked at just the right time of year, the leaves of this tea from a well-known estate in the northeastern Dimbula region are long and handsome, producing a liquor with subtle body and exquisite flavour.
An afternoon tea.

T307 PETTIAGALLA, OP
The short leaves of this tea from the famous garden yield a sustained yet delicate, mild taste.
Recommended for brunch.

T313 DIMBULA, BOP
A great estate on the high plateaus. A fully developed flavour–fruity, direct, brisk.
Ideal in the morning.

T316 RADELLA, BOP
Another great Dimbula estate, producing a tea typical of the high plateaus–golden in colour and flavour.
An excellent morning tea.

T320 DIYAGAMA, BOP
A truly great broken-leaf tea from Dimbula.
A bold, golden liquor.
Excellent in the morning.

T321 THERESIA, BOP
A Dimbula estate well-known for its smooth, fragrant tea.
Perfect on awakening.

T3182 UDA RADELLA, BOPF
Radella is famous for its fannings, which produce an amber liquor with strong, 'high grown' flavour and sustained aroma.
An ideal breakfast tea.

T322 SOMERSET, PEKOE
Short leaves. A full-bodied, aromatic tea for fans of very strong tea.

T323 LOINORN, PEKOE
Grown on the high plateaus of Bogawantalawa, this tea boasts body, powerful flavour, and grand aroma.
A strong, early-morning tea.

Uva

Uva, a region to the east of Dimbula, produces teas that are famous the world over. The best period coincides with the monsoon. From June to September, the southwest monsoon drops rain onto the west coast of the island while dry winds blow in the east. It is these dry winds that give Uva teas their character, refined taste, and grand aroma.

T3081 SAINT JAMES, OP
An excellent, highly esteemed estate. Its tea gives a coppery, highly coloured and scented liquor with smooth, fully developed flavour.
Famously good any time of the day.

T3082 BLAIRMOND, OP
An estate from the Uda Pussellawa district in northern Uva. Its long, fine leaves are carefully handled to produce an aromatic, amber liquor. Perfect for five o'clock tea.

T309 DYRAABA, FP
A flowery pekoe from the Uva region yielding a balanced beverage, simultaneously fragrant and strong.
A morning tea.

T310 UVA HIGHLANDS, FP
The fine, rolled leaves of this tea from the high plateaus give it heart and body. A refined, fragrant tea for the morning.

T311 ATTEMPETTIA, FP
This well-known, high-altitude estate rolls its fine leaves into balls, yielding a strong, direct yet refined tea, drinkable any time of day.

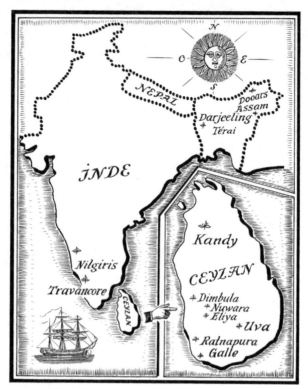

Tea Plantations in India and Ceylon.

T312 SAINT JAMES, BOP
The great character of this tea, from one of the island's leading estates, makes it a must. Highly aromatic, powerful, tasty. Excellent in the morning.

T3121 AISLABY, BOP
A grand tea from the high plateau of a remarkable estate. A brilliant, aromatic, powerful liquor of coppery colour. An exquisite choice to accompany a continental breakfast.

T314 UVA HIGHLANDS, BOP
A tea with great class, plucked at the best time of year. Its high plateau taste is round, intense, striking. Highly fragrant. A breakfast tea.

T3141 ADAWATTE, BOP
From the Badulla district in northern Uva, this highly fragrant tea with round, lively flavour is best appreciated in the morning.

T315 BOMBAGALLA, BOP
An Uva tea of outstanding quality, aromatic and full in the mouth. A morning tea.

T319 HIGH FOREST, BOP
A broken-leaf Uva tea known for its full-bodied, aromatic liquor. Just right for a continental breakfast.

T317   UVA HIGHLANDS, BOPF
   Fannings of truly high quality, producing a grand Uva tea.
Powerful and aromatic, delicious with a drop of cold milk.
A morning treat.

T318   DYRAABA, BOPF
   Fannings from the well-known garden. Very strong, fragrant tea that can act as a substitute for coffee.

Galle

Located on the southern part of the island, the Galle region specializes in Flowery Orange Pekoe and Orange Pekoe teas with handsome, well-proportioned leaves that are carefully sorted (which is not always the case in other regions). They thus merit special interest, especially since the French art of tea places particular importance on the beauty and harmonious appearance of the leaves themselves.

T300   BERUBEULA, FOP
   A rare tea from southern Ceylon, with very handsome, golden-tipped leaves. Superb nose, smooth taste, golden colour.
An excellent daytime tea.

T301   ALLEN VALLEY, FOP
   A very distinguished tea known for its fine appearance and mild, flowery flavour. A great five o'clock tea.

T3015   DEVONIA, FOP
   A wonderful harvest from Galle, very fine in appearance. A subtle aroma, refined taste, golden colour. Recommended for high tea.

T304   GALABODA, OP1
   A Galle tea plucked during the best season, yielding uniform leaves with flowery fragrance and good colour. The liquor has a rich, smooth taste and grand aroma, making it a perfect brunch tea.

T305   BERUBELLA, OP1
   A fine, whole-leaf tea from Matara, on the southern part of the island. Its amber liquor is fragrant and subtle. Ideal for a tea break.

Ratnapura

The Ratnapura district is some fifty miles east of Colombo, the capital. It is a low altitude region.

T308   RATNAPURA, OP
Long leaves producing a mild, exquisite aroma. A fine five o'clock tea.

• Detheinated Ceylon Teas

T340   THÉ DÉTHÉINÉ, OP
   Whole-leaf tea, 100% theine-free.

T350   THÉ DÉTHÉINÉ, BOP
   Broken-leaf tea, 100% theine-free.

JAPAN

Japanese tea, originally drunk by Zen Buddhist monks, was long the prerogative of lords and aristocrats.

*J*APAN, KINGDOM OF THE TEA ceremony, is the seventh-ranked producer of tea.

The only type of tea produced is green tea, or 'o cha'.

There are many varieties of green tea in Japan but export is very limited, given strong domestic demand.

The major tea growing regions are Shizuoka (which produces fully half the nation's output), Miye, Kagoshima, Kyoto, Uji, Nara, Saitama, and Fukuoka.

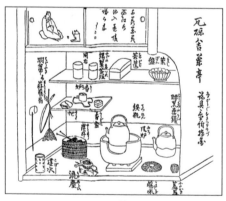

Tea equipage, Japan.

Green Japan tea is renowned for its delicate, exquisite aroma. It is also invigorating, aids digestion, and is mildly stimulating, thus helping to clear the mind.

Green Japan teas are very rich in vitamin C and naturally low in theine.

They are generally taken without sugar, and are ideal during or after a meal.

● *Whole-leaf Green Japan Teas*

T414   GYOKURO
'Precious Dew'

This tea is a veritable work of art from the Empire of the Rising Sun: only buds are plucked, very carefully by hand, and only once a year. The plants are placed under shade for three weeks prior to plucking in order to increase chlorophyll content and reduce tannin. The beautiful jade green leaves yield a liquor so subtle and smooth that it is the most noble, refined, and precious green tea in the world.

T4273   SENCHA UJI

An imperial Sencha from Tawaracho, a little village in Uji, near Kyoto, Japan's oldest tea-producing region. It is one of the highly respected Senchas. Its elegant leaves, with natural bloom, produce a slightly sweet liquor and grand, subtle aroma that fills the palate.

A magnificent tea, inducing serenity.

T4274   SENCHA YAME

Harvested in spring on a little family garden in the Fukuoka region, the leaves of this highly distinguished Sencha have a flowery nose.

They produce a tea of outstanding quality, with a fine green cup and mild flavour.

A perfect afternoon tea.

T4275 KAWANECHA
Known as the 'Darjeeling of Japan', this famous tea is grown along the Oi River in the Shizuoka region. It is characterized by elegant leaves, balanced taste, and intense yet subtle aroma. A delightful tea for those special moments.

T4276 SENCHA SAYAMA
A true rarity, this famous tea was the favourite beverage of the inhabitants of Edo (the former name of Tokyo from 1600 to 1867). Authentic Sencha Sayama is very difficult to find these days, because it is produced in extremely limited quantities. A grand tea, full of flavour and aroma, appropriate for special, relaxing moments.

T416 SENCHA HONYAMA
'The Emperor of Sencha teas' is the product of an exceptional harvest on a great Shizuoka garden. It yields a very rich liquor with grand aroma and exquisite flavour. A stimulating tea for the morning.

T417 SENCHA MIDORI
'The Shogun of Sencha teas' is a top quality green tea–highly fragrant, with delicate flavour. Very relaxing.

T418 SENCHA ARIAKE
Grown on the island of Kyushu, this Sencha is known for its fine bouquet, subtle, and flowery taste. Enjoyable all day long.

T419 TAMARYOKUCHA
One of spring's delights–young and fresh. Perfect anytime.

T420 YANAGICHA
An everyday green tea, with broad leaves, mild taste, marked aroma. Ideal during or after meals.

T421 SENCHA
The Japanese word Sencha means 'steeped tea'. The broad leaves give a brilliant liquor, rich in vitamin C, that delights connoisseurs of green tea. A typically Japanese flavour. Excellent quality.

T422 GENMAICHA
This extraordinary Japanese specialty is a mixture of fine quality green tea with toasted rice and popped corn. Its most original taste is also delicious when iced. Surprise your guests!

T424 FUJI-YAMA
A green tea for connoisseurs, grown near Mount Fuji. Its fine leaves, grand aroma, and subtle taste indicate its outstanding quality.

T425 HOJICHA
The broad leaves of this surprising tea have been toasted, producing a very pleasant taste. Naturally low in theine. An ideal accompaniment to meals.

T426 KUKICHA
The famous 'three year tea'. It has almost no theine, and is very calming. Light and fragrant. An evening tea.

T4277 URESHINOCHA
The taste of nostalgia. Grown on the island of Kyushu, this tea is unique in being processed according to the Chinese method–the freshly plucked leaves are 'roasted' (dry heat) rather than 'sweated' (steam) in the usual Japanese manner.
Highly appreciated by connoisseurs, its pale yellow liquor has a taste that remains long in the mouth. A rare tea for those rare occasions.

T4283 TENCHA UJI

A highly unusual tea insofar as its leaves have been broken into small pieces, normally prior to being pulverized to make Matcha powdered tea. Yet when steeped it makes a delicious tea, with an extremely light and mild cup. Ideal as an ingredient in recipes calling for tea.

• Powdered Japan Teas

T415 MATCHA UJI
'Froth of Liquid Jade'

This powdered tea is made only from tender young Gyokuro leaves, giving an imperial green tea for the famous tea ceremony. A dense, highly fragrant beverage, it is also delicious iced and as a flavouring for ice cream.

T423 MATCHA

'Matcha' simply means 'powdered tea', the type used in the famous Cha No Yu tea ceremony. A strong, concentrated beverage.

THAILAND KINGDOM OF SIAM

*I*N THE NORTH OF THE KINGDOM of Siam, on high mountain slopes, tea estates now stretch where opium crops once grew. Local ethnic minorities have handed down their traditional secrets, and tea enjoys an ideal climate here in the heart of the Golden Triangle.

Women having tea, Siam, 19th century

The limited yield is surprisingly original in nature. Thanks to the Buddhist tradition of offering oolong tea to monks, the Thai people have developed a special savoir-faire when it comes to partially oxidised teas. Now, prompted by the rich and flavourful local cuisine, the gustatory inventiveness of the Thais and the creative impulse of MARIAGE FRÈRES have produced a remarkable selection of black, green, and flavoured teas of great appeal.

T460 CHA THAÏ, BOPF

This original, highly esteemed tea serves as the ambassador of Thai taste. Reflecting the kingdom's joie-de-vivre, it is prepared with theatrical, delightful gestures on roadside tea stalls. It should be drunk hot, sugary and milky, or iced. This true elixir of happiness has a unique flavour of malt and chocolate. Cha Thai is a ticket to travel in the Land of Free Men.

T461 THAÏ BEAUTY

This miraculous tea is picked just once a year, then 30% oxidised. It has a brilliant, golden yellow liquor.

It aroma, intensified by long duration in the mouth, suggests the scent of magnolias and recalls the honey of litchi flowers, with a final note of white peach. Steep five grams of tea in 20 cl. of water for two to three minutes. With the blessings of the gods (climate, altitude, red soil), a new king of teas is born.

T462 OPIUM HILL

As soft as Thai silk. On the summits of misty slopes formerly devoted to growing poppies, this opium-producing land now yields a partially oxidised tea (15%) composed solely of young, tender leaves. Its frank, pale jade liquor, similar to a budding white peony, has a sappy freshness. Steep five grams of tea in 20 cl. of water for two to three minutes. The opium of tea!

T4620 THAÏ ORCHIDÉE

This outstanding blue tea from the Thai hills in the Golden Triangle is proof of the magic of local soil and climate. Its skilfully worked leaves produce a highly sensual cup marked by a floral note that recalls orchids. Fresh and mild, it is also long in the mouth. The product of just one annual plucking, Thaï Orchidée is made especially for MARIAGE FRÈRES in limited quantities. Supreme elegance.

T4631 CHA KIO

In Thailand, offerings for monks are set in front of temples: sugar, rice, fruit, fresh produce, incense, and this green tea drunk by tribal peoples from the Golden Triangle. As the only nourishment taken in the afternoon, it

is indispensable to everyday life. Popular throughout Thailand, Cha Kio is composed of ball-shaped leaves that produce a sparkling, balanced liquor with a flowery, bitter-free flavour similar to China oolongs. A slender bridge between body and soul.

T463 SIAM CLUB

On the border of Thailand and Burma, mountain dwellers have been privately growing a marvellous green tea, to which MARIAGE FRÈRES has delicately added tea flowers.
The golden, flowery, fragrant cup is lively yet delicate. Welcome to the exclusive society of Siam Club-lovers!

T464 LAN NA THAÏ

A million rice paddies stretching across the vast former Kingdom of Lan Na enrich this grand green tea with their lush fragrance of moist shoots.
The tea's mysterious smoothness, drunk hot or cold, is a mark of eternal friendship. Thirst-quenching both during and between meals, it represents MARIAGE FRÈRES tribute to Siam's legendary hospitality.

BURMA

*T*HE LAND OF GOLDEN TEMPLES has some of the most secluded tea estates in the world. Tea-cultivation has been jealously guarded on the high plateaus of the Golden Triangle straddling China and Laos. The Shan mountain tribes produce this tea in extremely limited quantities, for their own personal use. This exclusive tea has never before left the land on which it was grown.

T404　KO KANT

Burma's secret treasure. Of Shan origin, harvested almost wild, this sophisticated green tea from the Golden Triangle is unique. Prepared according to age-old methods, using only hands and a wok, the young, long, twisted leaves evoke the fragrance of mountain flowers. The liquor, gold like the pagodas of Pagan, gives off a sweet bouquet both flowery and grassy, suggesting the coolness of a dappled wood. Absolutely authentic.

KOREA

*K*OREA, KNOWN AS 'THE MOUNTAINOUS Peninsula', produces a very limited quantity of tea, which is very rarely exported.

T405　IRI

A green tea with character, halfway between China and Japan teas. Its young leaves yield a fine liquor with smooth taste. Invigorating.

LAOS

*L*AOS, IN THE HEART OF INDOCHINA, has two distinct tea-growing regions. To the far north, in the Golden Triangle, is the remote province of Phôngsali, wrapped in persistent mists during the rainy seasons and populated by over twenty different ethnic groups that continue to grow traditional opium crops as well as a unique, little-known tea. On a more organised level, the Bolaven

'Gouverneur' Teapot Created by MARIAGE FRÈRES.

plateau in the centre of Laos is home to tea gardens that were established thanks to experiments by French engineers in the 1920s. Here, in fertile soil, villagers perpetuate the skills of making green tea. The estates remain small, often family-run affairs.

T408　CHAMPASAK

This outstanding green tea, produced by ethnic minorities, is grown on the high plateaus of Bolaven. Its leaves, heated on a plate fuelled by a scented wood fire, are stirred for hours with little bamboo forks. The fertile red soil, watered by the monsoon rains, gives the tea an intense, slightly smoky taste with fragrances of mossy earth combined with flowery overtones. A rarity – available in limited quantities only – Champasak is a symbol of hospitality.

T409　PHONG SALY

This uniquely crafted green tea comes from estates scattered over the hills of Phôngsali (Phong Saly). Rolled by hand, processed in a wok, the leaves are sweated then dried over coals, sheathed in green-bamboo moulds whose sap slowly imparts a peppery flavour. Once dried, the tea is removed from the mould and then tied with a strip of bamboo. It yields a golden yellow liquor with a wild, woody yet delicate taste that remains long in the mouth. A truly ethnic tea.

Black Teas from Various Asian Countries

INDONESIA

*A*S THE SIXTH LEADING PRODUCER of tea, Indonesia's first estate was planted by the Dutch back in 1824. The main tea growing regions are located on the islands of Java and Sumatra. On Java, the extremely dry months of July, August, and September are most propitious for harvesting top quality teas. On Sumatra, situated between the second and third parallels south of the equator, tea is produced all year long. Once again, however, teas plucked during the driest months are considered to be the finest.

T411 TALOON, TGFOP
A tea harvested at just the right moment on a grand Javanese estate. Its fine whole leaves have golden tips, giving an aromatic, slightly sweet and bronzed flavour. Perfect for five o'clock tea.

T412 MALABAR, OP
This whole-leaf tea, from a famous garden on western Java, has a pure yet fairly strong taste. An afternoon tea.

T413 BAH BUTONG, BOP
A broken-leaf tea from Sumatra. Strong, dark, and slightly flowery. Recommended as a morning beverage.

BANGLADESH

*O*RIGINALLY CALLED EAST PAKISTAN when the Indian subcontinent was partitioned in 1947, Bangladesh–where Pakistani tea estates were located–later won its independence from the rest of Pakistan. Bangladesh's main tea growing region is Sylhet, other estates being found near Chittagong.
Plucking begins in early April and continues into December.
But the second harvest (May-June) is the finest–the tea is high in colour and fully aromatic.
Bangladeshi teas are often used as the basis of blends.
Their quality is comparable to teas from southern India.

'One drinks tea to escape the maddening world'   *T'ien Yi-Heng*

T401   CHITTAGONG, GFOP
     A rich black tea from one of the poorest countries in the world. Its whole leaves yield an aromatic, slightly spicy tea. May be taken with a drop of milk. A daytime tea.

MALAYSIA

*T*HANKS TO MALAYSIA'S IDEAL climate, the British began growing tea there in 1914.
The gardens are located on the cool heights of the Cameron Highlands in the hilly centre of the country.
Teas are harvested all year round.

T430   ULU BERNAM, BOP
     A black, broken-leaf tea from the Malay peninsula, producing a thick, strong, pungent liquor. Perfect in the morning, with a drop of milk.

NEPAL

*T*EA CROPS, ENCOURAGED BY THE Nepalese government, dot the Himalayan slopes. Nepal's estates produce mild, aromatic black teas. Only a very limited quantity is exported, given strong domestic demand.

' I am in no way interested in immortality, only in the taste of tea'

Lu T'ung,
a 'Tea-Crazed' 8th-century poet.

Plucking tea, 1930.

T431   MALOON, FTGFOP
     A great rarity, this top-quality tea is similar to a Darjeeling.
Its whole leaves produce a subtle fragrance and a flavour of ripe fruit. A fine tea all day long.

SIKKIM

*T*HIS TINY INDIAN STATE IN THE eastern Himalaya produces Darjeeling-type teas. Export quantities are extremely limited.

T471   TEMI, TGFOP
     This fine quality, Darjeeling-type tea is quite rare. Its handsome, golden-tipped leaves are flowery and aromatic, with the flavour of ripe fruit. A tea for festive occasions.

VIETNAM

HE FRENCH INITIALLY ESTABLISHED tea plantations in Vietnam in 1825. But given the conflicts that wracked the country throughout the nineteenth and twentieth centuries, the tea industry never really developed.

T4909 DALAT
This green tea from the high plateaus of the former French Indochina is not unlike green China teas.
The Vietnamese consider it to be their national beverage, drinking it all day to quench their thirst and relieve fatigue.

T4910 PLEIKU
A blue tea from the high plateaus of the province of Annam. This famous Oolong-style tea testifies to the influence of the Chinese skills in Vietnam.
It has a fragrance evoking wild orchids, and its finely twisted leaves produce an indescribable flavour of hazelnuts.
A fine beverage to accompany meals.

T4911 ANNAM, OP
This black tea has little, Chinese-style leaves that yield a mild yet dark liquor with a pronounced native tang. A daytime tea.

'Karawan'
a MARIAGE FRÈRES' recreation
of a 1875 orientalist style teapot

'Tea is as bitter as life, as strong as love and as sweet as death'
Arabian poet

'Ecstasy is a glass full of tea and a piece of sugar in the mouth'
Alexander Pushkin (1799-1837)

'They were seated around a table, drinking tea and talking of love'
Heinrich Heine (1797-1856)

'A tea ceremony is a communion of feelings, when good friends come together at the right moment under the best conditions'
Yasunari Kawabata (1899-1972)

Asia Minor

RUSSIA

*R*USSIA, LAND OF THE SAMOVAR, is a great consumer of what is traditionally called 'Russian tea' even though no tea grows there.

Starting in 1893, however, plantations were established along the Black Sea coasts of Georgia, in the northern Caucasus, and in Azerbaijan near the Caspian Sea.

Mechanical harvesting has made this region the seventh-ranked producer in the world.

French consumers often confuse 'Russian tea' with 'Russian Blend', a citrus-flavoured blend of various teas that are not grown in the region.

T451 GÉORGIE, OP

A real 'Russian' tea from Georgia. Its narrow leaves produce a dark yet mild liquor with distinctive taste. An evening tea.

T452 GÉORGIE, BOP

A broken-leaf Russian tea, fairly strong, with a pleasant, flowery flavour. A morning tea.

PERSIA

*A*LL GROWING AREAS ARE FOUND in the north of the country, between the Elburz Mountains and the Caspian Sea. Tea was introduced into the country in 1900, and is grown on small estates.

T441 ELBOURZ, OP

A good quality tea from the Caucasus region. Light and mild. An afternoon tea.

Packets of tea, Russia, 1920.

TURKEY

TURKEY IS THE WORLDS' FIFTH leading producer of tea. Since 1938, its gardens have been concentrated near Rize in eastern Anatolia, on the Black Sea coast.

Turkey produces only black tea, very little of which is exported due to high domestic consumption.

As in Georgia, tea is traditionally made in a samovar.

Around the Samovar, Caucasus, 1887.

T481   RIZÉ, OP
A fine quality Ottoman tea from the Black Sea region.
Its slender leaves yield a mild, slightly sweet liquor.
The perfect tea for an evening among friends.

T482   RIZÉ, BOP
A broken-leaf tea from northern Turkey.
Strong, not unlike Russian teas, and perfect for preparing with a samovar.
A morning tea.

———————

The first cup moistens my lips and throat

The second cup breaks my solitude and boredom

The third cup searches my entrails, barren for being nourished on nothing

but thousands of ideographs

With the fourth cup a slight perspiration arises, dissipating through my pores the afflictions and frustrations of a lifetime

The fifth cup purifies me totally

With the sixth cup I am transported to the realm of immortality

And with the seventh I can drink no longer

A cool, gentle breeze caresses my body

Immense serenity.

Lu T'ung

Poet from the Tang dynasty

Latin America

Argentina

*A*RGENTINA HAS BEGUN producing tea only recently. Ninety-five percent of its output is grown in Misiones, the rest coming from the border zone between Misiones and Corrientes in northwestern Argentina.

The finest harvests are plucked in the second half of October and November, producing dark and handsome leaves.

T501   MISIONES, BOP
A black, broken-leaf tea with fairly strong yet well-balanced flavour. A morning tea.

Tea arriving at the London Docks, 1850.

Brazil

*B*RAZIL IS LATIN AMERICA'S number two producer of tea, which is grown in the southwestern part of the state of Sao Paulo, below the Tropic of Capricorn. The local tea is known for its clear, brilliant liquor. The finest harvests are produced between November and March.

T511   SAO PAULO, BOP
A black, broken-leaf tea. Firm and friendly, just right for breakfast.

Ecuador

*T*EA CROPS WERE INTRODUCED into Ecuador in 1968. Most of its production is exported to the United States.

T530   APROANDES, BOP
This black, broken-leaf tea is highly aromatic. Its amber liquor carries a local tang. A stimulating, wake-up tea.

Africa

English planters, circa 1900.

CAMEROON

THE FIRST ESTATE IN CAMEROON was established back in 1928, and production has expanded ever since. The country is one of the leading producers of high quality teas in Africa. The three tea-growing regions are Tole, Ndu, and Djutitsa, in western Cameroon. The red laterite and volcanic soil of these equatorial regions gives them their special warm, round taste.
The finest harvest are plucked at the end of the dry season in late March and early April.

T600   MONT CAMEROUN, BOPF
An excellent tea from the volcano of Mount Cameroon (13,200 feet), called the 'Chariot of the Gods' by Carthaginian sailors. Grown at 3,500 feet above sea level, this black, broken-leaf tea is bright and highly aromatic, with a malty taste. It may be taken with a drop of milk. Highly appreciated by the English royal family.

KENYA

AS AFRICA'S LEADING PRODUCER, Kenya is known for the reliable quality of its teas throughout the year. The best harvests occur early in the dry season, either in late January and early February or in the month of July.

T601   MARINYN, GFOP
This grand garden produces the best and most refined black tea in Kenya. Its handsome, gold-tipped leaves yield a fine, brisk liquor. A daytime tea.

T602   HIGHGROWN, PEKOE
A black tea from the high plateaus of Kenya. A well-balanced, fruity taste, strong enough to be appreciated in the morning. Fine with a drop of milk.

MAURITIUS

*M*AURITIUS RANKS TWENTY-NINTH among tea producers. Tea was introduced to the island, formerly called Ile-de-France when under French control, by Pierre Poivre in 1770.

T606   GRAND BOIS CHÉRI, BOP
A broken-leaf tea with a distinct vanilla taste. Strong yet refined, this black tea is a morning drink.

MOZAMBIQUE

*M*OZAMBIQUE RANKS TWENTY-eighth among tea producers.

T611   GURUE, BOP
This pleasantly strong black tea has slightly spicy flavour. A morning tea.

MALAWI

*M*ALAWI IS AFRICA'S NUMBER TWO tea producer, just behind Kenya. Tea is harvested all year round, but the finest pluckings take place between May and September. Malawi's teas are similar to those from Ceylon.

T641   NAMINGOMBA, BOP
A black, English-style tea greatly appreciated in Britain. Its bright, coloury liquor is strong enough to take a drop of milk, and is just right for breakfast.

UGANDA

*U*GANDA IS RANKED THIRTEENTH among tea producers. Tea is grown mainly on large estates on the heights overlooking Lake Victoria.

T651   MITYANA, BOP
A straightforward black tea with spicy taste. An ideal substitute for coffee, it can take a drop of milk.

RWANDA

*R*WANDA RANKS SEVENTEENTH-among the world's tea producers.

T661   KITABI, BOP
An aromatic, black, broken-leaf tea. Perfect on awakening, with or without milk.

TANZANIA

*T*ANZANIA IS THE WORLD'S fourteenth-ranked tea producer.

T671   ITONA, BOP
This black tea from the high plateaus is strong and fruity, not unlike Ceylon teas. Taken with a drop of milk, it is perfect for a continental breakfast.

ZIMBABWE

*Z*IMBABWE IS RANKED SIXTEENTH among tea-producing countries.

T681   SOUTHBOWN, FANNINGS
The leaves have been crushed to produce a strong, British-style tea for lovers of full-bodied black teas. To be taken with milk.

SOUTH AFRICA

• Red Tea (Rooibos)

*T*HIS UNUSUAL 'TEA' DOES NOT come from the Camellia Sinensis tea plant; rather, it is made from a bush known variously in Latin as Aspalathus Linearis, Aspalathus Contaminatos, and Borbonia Pinifolia. It is grown at an altitude of 1,500 feet and the harvest takes place in February or March. The beverage has no stimulating effects, for it is absolutely free of theine and contains very little tannin. It is nevertheless very rich in vitamin C, mineral salts, and protein. Red tea can be drunk hot or cold, morning or evening, with or without milk. Perfect for children.

T621 THÉ ROUGE
Highly appreciated in South Africa, this 'red tea' has a mild, aromatic flavour and is 100% theine-free.

T631 CAPETOWN
A delicious red tea flavoured with bergamot, making it as delicate and elegant as Earl Grey. 100% theine-free. A perfect five o'clock tea.

T632 RICHMOND
A striking red tea flavoured with cinnamon and orange. Full yet refined taste, 100% theine-free. A convivial beverage.

T633 BOURBON
Flavoured with 'Bourbon vanilla', this red tea displays great finesse. Delicate aroma, subtle taste. 100% theine-free. For pleasant occasions.

T634 BLOEMFONTEIN
A 'Russian blend' (flavoured with various citrus fruits) that is 100% theine-free. Divine any time of the day.

T635 KIMBERLEY
An exotic red tea flavoured with fruit and flowers from distant lands. 100% theine-free. A fine beverage.

T636 MARCO POLO ROUGE
'Marco Polo Red' is MARIAGE FRÈRES own masterpiece. A wonderful tea. 100% theine-free.

T637 MÉTIS
This 'cross-breed', as its name implies, is a fine hybrid of red tea with fruit, citrus fruit, spices, and flowers. A heady garden, 100% theine-free.

T638 NIL ROUGE
Scents of citrus, Oriental spices, and marigolds complement this 'Red Nile' tea, extending a voyage begun with Thé sur le Nil (T955). Its simultaneously lively yet mild taste offers an exotic range of flavours for late-night dreams of distant lands.

T639 SURABAYA
Surabaya, lapped by the Java Sea, dotted with Dutch-style houses and Islamic minarets, is steeped in 1930s charm. It forever sways to the tune of lost illusions expressed by the famous Brecht/Weill love song 'Surabaya Johnny'. In memory of that evocative past, MARIAGE FRÈRES has created this red tea sprinkled with petals of mallow flower, giving off a scent of exotic blossoms and vanilla-drenched spices.

Gelée Extra de Thé

BOURBON

Oceania

Australia

*T*EA PLANTS WERE INTRODUCED into Bingil Bay in 1884 by the four Cutten brothers, who ran a 3,000-acre agricultural empire. Australia now ranks thirtieth among tea-producing countries. Its plantations are all located in the state of Queensland.

T690   NERADA, BOP
A rare tea from the foothills of majestic Bartle Frere Mountain (5,300 feet) in northern Queensland. Grown in red, volcanic soil, this black tea has a bright, colourly liquor and strong, aromatic flavour.
Takes a drop of milk.
Fine for breakfast.

Papua-New Guinea

*P*APUA-NEW GUINEA IS RANKED twenty second among tea producers.

T695   KINDENG, FANNINGS
The crushed leaves of this black tea yield a very dark, strong, aromatic liquor.
A morning tea.

'He who has nothing left still has tea'

Chinese proverb

— 86 —

GRAND TRADITION

Over 150 years of experience have enabled Mariage Frères *to offer its sophisticated clientele a range of subtle, refined blends. Each blend has been given a specific, exclusive name.*
Mariage Frères *blends employ only the best teas from the finest gardens, orchestrating harmonious flavours sought by discriminating French palates. Now you, too, can appreciate this wonderful alchemy, the fruit of over a century of loving care.*

• Classic Morning Blends

T7000 FRENCH BREAKFAST TEA
This perfect marriage of great and elegant black teas produces a rounded taste of malt and chocolate. Its highly developed flavour is both powerful and refined.
A felicitous blend in the best tradition of the French art of tea. With or without milk, perfect with a continental breakfast.

T700 BREAKFAST EARL GREY
A magnificent, noble marriage of full-bodied Ceylon tea and the delicate scent of bergamot. An ideal morning beverage, strong yet refined.

T701 MORNING TEA
A brilliant blend of the finest Broken Orange Pekoes from renowned estates in Ceylon and India.
Full flavour, bold aroma.
Welcomes a drop of cold milk.

T702 ENGLISH BREAKFAST TEA
This full-bodied, British blend is strong on colour and aroma. Serve steaming hot with milk, along with toast and marmalade.
For connoisseurs.

T7023 DE LONDRES
This fine 'London' tea is a blend of famous teas from China, Cameroon, and India, yielding a strong yet refined brew. Fine with a drop of cold milk.

T7024 THÉ CÉLADON
Chrysanthemum flowers enhance this 'celadon-green' sencha.
A flowery scent sweetens the stimulating green beverage. Its pale green liquor evokes the hue called celadon.
Oriental sages called it 'the finest shade of jade' in honour of its shimmering highlights of green, blue, and grey - a source of purity and beauty.
Adds a touch of poetry to the morning's repast.

T703 SULTANE

The 'sultaness' is MARIAGE FRÈRES' traditional breakfast blend of fine Ceylon teas. Its strong flavour has a slightly chocolate taste. Best with a continental breakfast, with or without milk.

T704 KAISER

This invigorating tea is based on an old German blend. Full-bodied yet refined, it can be taken with or without milk.

T705 EMPEREUR CHEN NUNG

This majestic blend is named after the Chinese emperor who discovered tea in 2737 bc. It has a subtle aroma and delicate, slightly smoky flavour. A perfect companion for a hearty, savory breakfast. Without milk.

T706 DUKE OF WELLINGTON

A powerful blend of three Broken Orange Pekoes from India and Ceylon, along with a green China tea. A strong, direct brew that makes a good substitute for coffee.

T7063 GOUVERNEUR

A vigorous, original blend of fine teas from Yunnan and Assam. Rich, rounded, and smooth, with a golden glow. Can take a drop of cold milk.

T7064 LE CONSUL

A superb composition of high grown teas from China, India, and Indonesia. A glorious blend of strength and subtlety.

T7065 WASHINGTON

A highly sophisticated blend of Flowery Orange Pekoes from India and Ceylon. Rich yet subtle, perfect for lunch. May be taken with milk.

T7067 PONDICHÉRY

Named after the French trading post in India, this nostalgic blend of several whole-leaf Indian teas has a round and smooth flavour. With or without milk.

T707 WEDDING

A balanced composition of the finest Ceylon teas. A pleasant taste that is neither too strong nor too mild. May be wedded to milk.

T708 BRASILIA

A brisk, energetic blend of high plateau teas with Brazilian maté. A very strong tea, high in theine. A stimulant on awakening, preferably without milk. Fine with breakfast.

T7083 PARAMARIBO

A colonial blend of African teas, each with its own character. A full-bodied flavour with a hint of vanilla. With or without milk.

T7085 GUERRIERS

'Warriors' means strength–this blend of crushed-leaf teas from the high plateaux of Asia and plains of Africa yields a dark, strong, aromatic brew. To awaken the warrior in you.

T709 MAJESTY

A fascinating English blend of Ceylon teas with slightly smoky China teas. Perfect for a full English breakfast.

T7091 THÉ DE L'AVENTURIER

A 'Buccaneer's tea' full of colonial sunshine.

'Fils de France' Teapot, designed to celebrate the 140th anniversary of MARIAGE FRÈRES.

A sensational blend of fine whole-leaf teas from high plateaux.
Stimulating yet refined, to be taken without milk.
A tea from across the seas.

T7093 MAISON DE THÉ
In Imperial China, 'Tea Houses' welcomed a cross-section of society and served a variety of snacks, from sweet cakes to savory dim sum (meat dumplings).
This blend of teas from China and Formosa is designed to go well with both sweet and spicy dishes.

T7095 ROI DE SIAM
'King of Siam' is a regal combination of five kingly teas from China, Formosa, and India.
Deliciously smoky, this is a refined morning blend. Without milk.

T7097 SUCCESSEUR
A smoky, aromatic blend of great character. A strong, refined, stunning tea. Without milk.

T7099 LU YU
A divine blend named after the eighth-century 'apostle of tea'.
A mixture of highly smoky and bergamot-flavoured teas. Strong and fragrant. Without milk.

• Classic Daytime Blends

T710 AFTERNOON TEA
A blend of teas from Ceylon and India. Fairly full-bodied, aromatic–perfect for the afternoon.

T711 LUNCH TEA
An attractive blend of whole-leaf teas from Ceylon and India.
Smooth, aromatic flavour.
Designed to accompany lunch.

T712 FIVE O'CLOCK TEA
A delicious blend of the finest high-grown Ceylon teas.
A choice, sophisticated tea.

T7123 FILS DE FRANCE
'Son of France' was the name of a famous ship that brought China teas to MARIAGE FRÈRES in 1827.
This blend is composed of discreetly scented high-grown teas from India and China. A noble tea.

T7124 GRANDS AUGUSTINS
This magnificent blend was created in honour of the opening of the new MARIAGE FRÈRES shop on Rue des Grands Augustins on the Left Bank of Paris.
Its fragrance evokes the spices and atmosphere of the French East India Company in the seventeenth century–an aromatic voyage through time and space.

T7125 ROI-SOLEIL
'The Sun King', Louis XIV, was reportedly one of the first Frenchman to drink tea.

This haughty blend is based on the power of golden Yunnan teas and the flowery note of a famous smoky China tea, sprinkled with tips of green tea. Heavenly.

T713 IMPÉRATRICE
'Empress' is a subtle blend of delicately scented teas from China and India. A mild tea with delightful taste.

T7133 HAUTE MER
'High Seas' is a symphonic blend of teas from across the ocean.
Full yet refined flavour. A dreamy tea.

T714 MAHARAJAH
A harmonious blend of fine Indian teas, very round in the mouth.

T7143 GENTLEMAN
A fine, masculine blend of Flowery Orange Pekoes from India, China, and Ceylon.
With or without milk.

T715 SOUVERAINE
A velvety wedding of China and Ceylon teas, dotted with jasmine flowers.
Light and fragrant.

T7153 TEA PARTY
This festive blend is a mixture of teas from China and Formosa.
A delicate fragrance. Without milk.

T716 GRAND MANDCHOU
'Grand Manchu' is a traditional Chinese blend combining fine teas from different regions of the country.
Slightly smoky, with silver tips.
Great finesse.

T717 AMBASSADEUR
A lush blend of the finest Russian and China teas.
Mild yet slightly sweet flavour.

T718 AMATEUR
A thrilling blend of black and green teas, sprinkled with jasmine flowers.
Slightly smoky, highly appreciated by connoisseurs.

T719 SMOKY EARL GREY
A strange and surprising blend of smoky China and bergamot-scented tea.
A highly pronounced aroma.

T720 KINGSTON
A refined English blend of mild teas from China, India, and Ceylon, plus a sprinkling of silver tips.
Rich aroma. Real class.

T721 « 1854 »
A magnificent blend of extremely fine Indian and China teas, delicately sprinkled with jasmine flowers and silver tips.
Subtle fragrance, refined taste.
A supreme homage to the year the MARIAGE FRÈRES firm was founded.

T722 CHA KING
This esoteric, highly sophisticated, slightly smoky blend of three categories of China tea is named after the famous 'Holy Scripture of Tea' written by the great Chinese poet Lu Yu during the Tang era.
Wonderful flavour.

T723   PRINCE BHODI-DHARMA
A divine blend of regal teas–
Grand Darjeeling and Grand Yunnan.
Highly appreciated for its subtle aroma
and exquisite taste.

T724   MIKADO
An enchanting, traditional blend
from the Japanese imperial court.
Composed of the finest China
teas–from both Formosa and the
mainland–it is highly aromatic and has
a most pleasant taste.

T725   GENGIS KHAN
Invigorating. According
to Chinese legend, Genghis
Khan had his warriors drink
tea to instil them with courage
and effectiveness in battle.
This slightly smoky blend is
sprinkled with jasmine flowers
and silver tips. 'An iron fist in
a velvet cup'.

T7253 ZODIAC
A handsome blend of
teas from India and China,
pleasantly smoky and
scented. Smooth and subtle.

T7254 KARIKAL
A blend recalling the splendour of
a former French trading post in
India–ships carrying tea to France often
called at Karikal.
This blend successfully weds the
refinement of a high-grown Grand
Darjeeling to the briskness of a green tea
from Assam, the whole thing
underscored by subtle lotus flowers.
A tea designed to accompany a meal.

T7255 BIRTHDAY TEA
A history of savoir-faire.
This nostalgic blend was inspired by
the 141st anniversary of the founding of
MARIAGE FRÈRES.
A festive tea now associated with
every birthday and anniversary worth
celebrating, this harmonious blend adds
the fragrance of rare citrus fruit and
spices to the refined bouquet of first
flush Darjeelings.
A hint of honey and ginger bread.
The perfect balance.

T7256 LE VOYAGEUR
In honour of
enchanted travellers, this
distinguished blend
symbolizes escape and
freedom.
It subtly combines the
finest 'teas of mountain
mists' with the most
refined 'teas beneath
the clouds', underscored
by an unforgettable
fragrance.
A spur to voyagers.

T7257 À LA PORTE CHINOISE
'At the Chinese Gate' was the
sign of a 19th-century merchant
of tea and 'Products from China
and the Indies'.
This blend is a supreme homage to
China teas and to the mysterious charm
of the East.
It carefully marries fives types of China
tea: white, green, Oolong, black, and
flavoured.
Its majestic aroma transports whoever
drinks it to a garden of exotic teas.

T7258 LA ROUTE DU TEMPS
'The Path of Time' was created in memory of Richard Bueno to celebrate the 10th anniversary of MARIAGE FRÈRES' left-bank boutique, which he founded. A tea between two worlds, blending the flowery, honeyed taste of green teas from the Golden Triangle with the spicy note of pieces of ginger, which dot it like stones along a path.

T7259 LUNE ROUGE
'Red Moon' is a green tea grown on hillsides in the Golden Triangle, from whence it follows an age-old caravan route to Tibetan monasteries. Its flowery, spicy taste has a flavour of honey balanced by ginger and scented with rose. For those timeless moments.

T7260 ANGKOR
Invented in the spirit of the magnificent Angkor civilisation, this green tea with accents of wild spice features the smooth scent of young rice and tea flowers. A sensual tea.

• Classic Evening Blends

T726 EVENING TEA
A soothing blend of handsome leaf teas from China, India, and Ceylon. Its round yet mild flavour is perfect for evening.

T727 RAJINI
This refined 'Queen's tea', as the Sanskrit names implies, is a blend of good quality Indian and China teas, lightly sprinkled with rose petals. A mild tea with subtle aroma and taste.

T728 TZAR ALEXANDRE
Our own Russian blend, featuring silver tips, is famous for its grand finesse and slightly smoky fragrance. This masterpiece by MARIAGE FRÈRES is named after the Russian czar who introduced Parisians to Russian-style tea in 1814.

T729 YANG-TSÉ-KIANG
A famous blend appreciated its relaxing effect by inhabitants of the Yang-Tse-Kiang valley. Fragrant and delicate.

T730 CHA DO
'The Way of Tea' is a meditative quest, as reflected in this blend of grand Indian and Formosa teas. Fine character, delicious taste and aroma.

T731 FONDATEUR
The serene qualities of this slightly smoky blend of great China teas makes it a must. A sophisticated taste with fruity overtones.

T732 GRANDE CARAVANE
This calming blend of fine teas from various regions of China is naturally low in theine. Light yet flavourful.

T733 SIVARA
A specially devised, exclusive blend that is naturally low in theine. Smooth and aromatic flavour. Highly refined.

T734 TA-CHA
Very low in theine, and highly appreciated for that very reason. A very light blend for evenings.

T735   GRAND SIÈCLE
The 1600s were France's 'Grand Century', echoed in this symphonic blend of grand Formosa teas and traditional China teas.
Divine grandeur.

T736   COMÈTE
This gentle 'Comet' is a harmonious blend of China and Formosa teas that are low in theine and delicately scented.

T737   DARLINGTON
A romantic blend of mild teas from India, Formosa and Japan.
A tea with great character.

T738   CONFUCIUS
An immortal, slightly smoky blend of classic teas from China and Formosa.
A tea with great character.

T739   NARCISSE
An exclusive blend of handsome China teas, fragrant and smoky.
Light and refined.

T740   NOSTALGIE
A nostalgic blend of teas from distant lands. Very low in theine.

T741   RENAISSANCE
A eulogy to tea. This poetic blend combines mild, subtle teas from China, Formosa, and Japan to create a suave, harmonious cup that is slightly sweet and fragrant.
For relaxing moments.

T742   MAHÉ
The magic of Mahe of Malabar, a former French trading post in India, famous for the pepper trade.
This evening blend evokes pleasant colonial days–refined black tea, smooth green tea, and young blue tea with a hint of the mystic odours of distant lands. A tea for reveries.

T743   THÉ DES POÈTES SOLITAIRES
A blend developed in honour of the 'Solitary Poets' who have written of tea's delights.
An evening blend of grand high-grown teas from China with the flowery note of a Darjeeling Oolong from the high plateaus of the Himalayas.
A mild, subtle tea that induces exotic and nostalgic daydreaming.

'Théière des Poètes Solitaires'.

T744   PLANTATION
A fragrant whiff of an old-fashioned estate. Created in honour of a devoted planter, this blend combines the finest and most reputable Darjeeling Oolongs and green Darjeelings.
A true evening splendour.

FLAVOURED TEAS

Ever since the dawn of time, the Chinese–founders of humanist civilization and bards of life's pleasures–have learned and have taught that bliss should be sought in nature. Tea, as a marvellous symbol of their ancestral customs, marries well with nature's subtle fragrances: both the tea and the scent are enhanced. The finest example of such an alliance is bergamot flavoured tea, known as Earl Grey.

GREAT CLASSICS

• Earl Grey: Bergamot Flavoured teas

T8001 ROI DES EARL GREY
'The King of Earl Greys' is magnificent. For the first time, a premier black tea from the high plateaux of Yunnan Province in China has been discreetly scented with MARIAGE FRÈRES' famous bergamot fragrance. A divine tea.

T8002 EARL GREY IMPÉRIAL
A grand tea. Darjeeling exquisitely flavoured with bergamot.

Gelée Extra de Thé

EARL GREY IMPÉRIAL

T8004 GRAND EARL GREY
A high quality Ceylon tea sprinkled with silver needle tips and scented with bergamot.

T8005 EARL GREY FRENCH BLUE
This velvety black tea, elegant and sophisticated, is cloaked in the fragrance of fine, rare bergamot and royal blue cornflowers.

T8006 EARL GREY OOLONG
Black Dragon tea from Formosa, delicately scented with bergamot.

T8007 EARL GREY SENCHA
A green China tea with a subtle fragrance of bergamot.

T8008 EARL GREY DÉTHÉINÉ
A theine-free Ceylon tea finely flavoured with bergamot.

T8009 EARL GREY PU-ERH
The fine bergamot used by MARIAGE FRÈRES now flavours a matured China tea. A world first, with notes both flowery and powerful, fresh and enveloping. Unique.

T700 BREAKFAST EARL GREY
Full-bodied Ceylon tea with strong bergamot flavour.

T817 EARL GREY HIGHLAND
A high plateau tea sublimely flavoured with bergamot.

T8175 ENGLISH EARL GREY
A blend of China and Darjeeling teas with bergamot flavour.

T8183 EARL GREY SILVER TIPS
The divine flavour of bergamot in a China tea sprinkled with silver needle tips.

T8185 EARL GREY
China tea with the exquisite flavour of bergamot.

T719 SMOKY EARL GREY
Earl Grey with a smoky taste.

• Jasmine Flavoured Teas

Crafted Teas

T8320 BOUQUET DE THÉ AU JASMIN
An imperial flower. Young leaves are hand crafted into a beautiful bouquet, delicately flavoured with jasmine. One bouquet per person should be steeped for 3 minutes in pure, 85°C (185°F) water.
The height of refinement.

T8321 BOURGEON DE THÉ AU JASMIN
A majestic bud. Young buds of subtly scented green tea are skilfully crafted into the shape of the bud of a jasmine flower. Once steeped for 3 minutes in pure, 85°C (185°F) water, the fragrance of this precious tea will transport you to the most secret of gardens.

T8322 ÉTOILE DE THÉ AU JASMIN
An imperial star. Handsome leaves of green tea are mildly scented with jasmine, then shaped into a star. Two stars per person should be steeped for five minutes in pure, 85°C (185°F) water.
A poetic, perfumed tea.

T8323 PERLE DE THÉ AU JASMIN
An imperial pearl. Age-old skill is required to shape young, fine tea, harmoniously scented with jasmine, into precious pearls.
Ten pearls per person should be steeped for 3 minutes in pure, 85°C water.
A suave, refined cup. Divine.

Leaf Teas

T8300 JASMIN IMPÉRIAL
'The King of Jasmine Teas' is made with very rare green tea.
A wonderful combination of this subtle tea and the most refined jasmine flowers.

T8301 JASMIN CHUNG FENG
'The Champagne of Jasmine Tea' comes from an outstanding harvest.
Exquisite fragrance.

T8302 THÉ DES MANDARINS
A white tea from Fujian Province. Precious buds called silver needles are

THÉ DES MANDARINS
BOUGIE PARFUMÉE

MARIAGE FRÈRES
MAISON FONDÉE EN 1854

magnificently scented with the tenderest jasmine flowers.
The prerogative of Mandarins.

T8303 JASMIN MONKEY KING
　　　The famous green jasmine tea from Hunan. Fabulously fragrant.

T8305 JASMIN HEUNG PIN
　　　A highly reputed green tea divinely flavoured with jasmine.

T8307 JASMIN GUANG XI
　　　A green tea from Guang Xi Province subtly scented with jasmine.

T8309 JASMIN HU BEI
　　　Green tea from Hu Bei Province with a grand jasmine flavour.

T8313 JASMIN MANDARIN
　　　A Chinese green tea with jasmine flowers.

T8315 JASMIN
　　　A green tea with jasmine flowers.

• Traditional Flavoured Teas

T2308 BLANC & ROSE (White tea)
T812 CHRYSANTHÈME (Chrysanthemum - green tea)
T821 FLEURS D'ORANGER OOLONG
　　　(Orange blossoms)
T835 LICHEE (Litchi)
T836 LOTUS ROYAL
T8361 LOTUS D'OR (Golden Lotus – green tea)
T837 MAGNOLIA (Green tea)
T856 ORCHIDÉE
T867 ROSE
T870 THÉ VERT À LA MENTHE
　　　(Green tea with mint)

Packing tea in chests, China, 1900.

FANCY FLAVOURS

A RICH RANGE OF fancy teas has filtered to Europe from deepest Asia, where subtle scents of fruit, flowers, plants, and roots are poetically plucked from Mother Nature.

May this extensive bouquet blossom in every refined palate.

T801	ABRICOT
T802	AMANDE (Almond)
T804	ANIS (Aniseed)
T805	BAIES SAUVAGES (Wild berries)
T806	BANANE
T807	CANNELLE (Cinnamon)
T808	CARAMEL
T809	CARDAMOME (Cardamom)
T810	CASSIS (Black currant)
T811	CERISE (Cherry)
T813	CHOCOLAT
T814	CITRON (Lemon)
T815	CITRON VERT (Lime)
T816	COING (Quince)
T820	ÉPICES (Spiced)
T822	FRAISE (Strawberry)
T823	FRAMBOISE (Raspberry)
T824	FRUIT DE LA PASSION
T825	GINGEMBRE (Ginger)
T826	GINSENG
T827	GROSEILLE (Red currant)
T838	MELON
T839	MANDARINE (Mandarin orange)
T840	MANGUE (Mango)
T841	MANGUE AMAZONE
T846	MIEL (Honey)
T847	MIRABELLE (Cherry plum)

T849	MÛRE SAUVAGE (Wild blackberry)
T850	MYRTILLE (Blueberry)
T852	NOIX (Walnut)
T853	NOIX DE COCO (Coconut)
T854	ORANGE
T855	ORANGE AMÈRE (Seville orange)
T857	PAMPLEMOUSSE (Grapefruit)
T859	PÊCHE (Peach)
T860	PEPPERMINT (Green tea)
T862	POIRE (Pear)
T863	POMME (Apple)
T864	RHUBARBE
T866	RHUM (Rum)
T868	SAKURA (Green tea flavoured with Japanese cherry blossoms)
T8680	SAKURA 2000 A blend of green tea and young cherry blossoms, symbol of freshness and rebirth.
T869	SAKURA IMPÉRIAL (High quality Sencha tea grandly flavoured with cherry blossoms)
T871	VANILLE DES ÎLES
T8712	VANILLE IMPÉRIALE
T8713	VANILLE SENCHA (Green tea)
T872	VIOLETTE
T873	YLANG-YLANG

FLAVOURED BLENDS

EA HAS ITS OWN SPECIAL FRAGRANCE, AS DO FLOWERS, FRUIT, AND SPICES. Nothing prevents a happy marriage of these fragrances when a master blender from MARIAGE FRÈRES is inspired to combine all these subtle elements.

T8201 CHANDERNAGOR
A successful blend of spices commemorating a famous French trading post in India–cloves, cinnamon, ginger, cardamom, and pepper. Warm in the mouth.

T901 APOLLON
Fruit and flower petals give this blend a subtle, artful aroma worthy of the god Apollo.

T902 ARCHIPEL
A blend of flowers from the Japanese archipelago. Refreshing and flowery.

T903 AIDA
An operatic composition of Mediterranean citrus fruit. Fragrant, well-balanced.

T904 BOLÉRO
A refreshing blend with the aroma of Mediterranean fruit. Velvety taste.

T905 BUTTERSCOTCH
Black Ceylon tea flavoured with chocolate and caramel. Surprisingly delicious.

T906 CANNELLE-ORANGE
China and Ceylon teas flavoured with selected orange and cinnamon oils. Invigorating, hot or cold.

T907 CARAÏBES
Caribbean fruit and flowers flavour teas from India and Ceylon. Exotic.

T908 CASABLANCA
A fine marriage of green tea with Moroccan mint and bergamot-flavoured tea. A refreshing surprise. 'Play it again'.

T909 CHOCO MENTHE
A very British combination of chocolate and mint flavoured tea.

T910 ÉQUATEUR
A blend of black China tea with green Japan tea, flavoured with fruit and flowers from equatorial regions. Very fruity and flowery.

T911 ÉROS
A blend for lovers, flavoured with hibiscus and mallow flowers.

T912 EXOTIQUE
Ceylon tea flavoured with exotic fruit, plus a sprinkling of magnolia flowers and rose petals. Most pleasant.

T913 FRUITS NOIRS
Black China and Ceylon teas flavoured with black currants, blackberries, and blueberries. Delicious.

T914 FRUITS ROUGES
A blend flavoured with strawberries, raspberries, red currants, and cherries.

T915 JAMAÏQUE
An Indian tea flavoured with extracts of choice vanilla and Jamaican rum.

T916 KABUKI
A composition of wild fruit from the Far East. Very refined.

T917 MANDALAY
A black Ceylon tea flavoured with the oils of rare Burmese spices. Incomparable taste–a true delight.

T918 MARCO POLO
MARIAGE FRÈRES' most famous secret is this mysterious blend that takes you to distant lands and strange countries. The aroma of Chinese and Tibetan flowers and fruit lend it a uniquely velvety taste. Its extraordinary bouquet makes Marco Polo the most legendary of flavoured teas.

MARIAGE FRÈRES
MF   MF
Gelée Extra de Thé
MARCO POLO

T919 MAYFLOWER
Black China tea flavoured with flowers from the Pacific Coast of the United States. Pleasantly surprising.

T920 NARINDA
The essences of various fruits lend a delicate aroma to this blend of Indian and Ceylon teas. Highly refined.

T921 NOËL
A festive tea blended specially for the occasion. Flavoured with mild Christmas spices, it includes pieces of orange zest and vanilla.

T922 ORIENTAL
An oriental blend of jasmine and mandarin orange. Marvellous.

T923 PARSIFAL
A great fragrance of vanilla, dotted with lavender flowers.

T924 PHÉNIX
A subtle composition of vanilla, caramel, and honey.

T925 PODRÉA
Black China tea scented with vanilla, jasmine, mandarin orange, rose, and bergamot. Very refined.

T926 RIVIÈRA
A delicious mixture of Mediterranean fruit.

T927 RUSCHKA
A secretive tea, scented with essences of citrus and other fruits, dotted with silver needles. Alluring.

T928 SÉRÉNADE
A royal blend of flowers. Sweet and flowery.

T929 SALADE DE FRUITS
A mixture of natural fruit essences. Wonderfully fruity.

T930 SAMOURAÏ
The grand fragrance of bergamot mixed with other rare essences. Fully developed aroma, splendid in the mouth.

T931 TROIS NOIX
A delicious blend of three nut flavours.

T932 TROPICAL
The heady fragrance of tropical fruit makes this tea a top flavoured blend. A fruity composition that fully merits its popularity.

T933 VIVALDI
A highly original orchestration of the essences of selected fruits. Harmonious aroma and flavour.

T934 VÉRANDA
A colonial blend of various fragrances from distant lands. Highly aromatic.

T935 YIN YANG
A fine marriage of exotic citrus fruits. Exquisite taste, exquisite balance.

T936 MIRABEAU
Green tea flavoured with liquorice and mallow. A flowery bouquet.

T937 VALENTIN
A romantic tea in which bergamot encounters mallow. Exquisite flavour.

T938 PHARAON
A magnificent alliance of green Indian tea and essences of fruit from the Nile delta. Most civilized.

T939 ARTÉMIS
Fine China and Ceylon teas apparelled in the delicate fragrance of fruits from distant lands. A mythical blend.

T940 PRINCE IGOR
A rich blend of green Japan tea and black Ceylon tea, flavoured with rare citrus and other fruits. Charismatic.

T9401 BALTHAZAR
An Oriental combination of toasted green Japan tea and black Ceylon tea, flavoured with exotic fruit. A glorious tea.

T9402 TRINIDAD
A secret blend of green Japan tea and black China tea, flavoured with island fruits and flowers. An enchanting, sunny tea.

T9403 MONTAGNE D'OR
'Golden Mountain' is a felicitous blend of traditional flavoured teas from China with fruits from the mountains of the Golden Triangle. A precious tea.

T941 YANAON
An elegant blend evoking the mysterious fascination for the former French trading post of Yanaon, to the north of Madras. High grown black and green teas are highlighted by majestic notes of exotic fragrances, sprinkled with festive flowers. A poetic, perfumed tea.

T942 THÉ DE PÂQUES
'Easter Tea' is a wonderful blend honouring the holiday spirit. MARIAGE FRÈRES created this special tea by blending subtle fragrances

of citrus and other fruits with a
distinguished note of noble spices,
evoking the taste of crème brûlée.
Perfect harmony.

T943 THÉ DE FÊTE
This 'Festive Tea' is pure magic.
Mariage Frères devised it in the spirit of
grand occasions where tea plays a
special role. The glamorous blend acts
as an ambassador of the French art of
tea. Magnificent essences of fruits and
spices from distant lands are
harmoniously orchestrated with a mild
China tea. A tea to celebrate.

T944 PLEINE LUNE
The splendour of a 'Full Moon'.
Inspired by that heavenly body and the
realm of dreams, this poetic blend
combines fragrances evoking the feast of
the full moon: fruits, rare spices, and the
sweet taste of honey. A true moonbeam.

T945 ÎLE MAGIQUE
The mystery of a 'Magic Isle'.
As a symbol of peacefulness, the
magic isle calls for a serene blend.
A mild China tea is flavoured
with delicate fragrances of Pacific
fruits and flowers. Pure paradise.

T946 BAL MASQUÉ
The fascination of an operatic
'Ballo in Maschera'–
lavender from Provence and vanilla

from Mauritius are disguised by
elegant veils of colonial fruit.
A sophisticated fragrance makes for an
enchanting tea.

T947 ÉLÉPHANT BLANC
According to a legend from
Siam, the capture of a magnificent
'White Elephant' guarantees the king a
long and prosperous reign.
This sentimental blend is composed of
essences of wild spices and festive
fruits–long may it reign.

T948 ÉLIXIR D'AMOUR
A lyrical 'Elisir d'Amore' inspired
by a love of tea. This fabulous blend
echoes love's idyllic message. A happy
marriage of fine tea and enigmatic
fragrances of legendary flowers.
A wonderfully magical tea.

T949 EXPOSITION COLONIALE
Nostalgic beauty: unveiled by
Mariage Frères on December 11, 1997,
this sublime blend evokes the spirit of the
cultural melting-pot of France's 'Colonial
Expositions'. A fragrant, poetic voyage to
the heart of the civilisations of tea. The
noble flavour of a first-flush Darjeeling
elegantly wed to the divine scent of rare
spices from the colonies. Perfect harmony.

T950 WEDDING IMPÉRIAL
A paean to love.
This glamorous blend is
steeped in the passion
that weds the malty
power of golden Assam
tea leaves to the
sweetness of notes of
chocolate and caramel.
Perfect clarity. Evidence
of a peerless marriage.

T951   ÉTOILE DE FRANCE

The 'Star of France' represents the essence of the French art of tea. Created on October 16, 1997 - a full moon - to celebrate the opening of MARIAGE FRÈRES Ginza in Tokyo, this tea illustrates French skill and savoir-faire. Tender green leaves of Japanese Sencha are combined with noble spices from France. Simplicity and perfection.

T952   THÉ À L'OPÉRA

A eulogy to sensuality. From spiritual beverage to lyrical elixir, the refinement of tea meets the melodic beauty of opera. A distinguished green tea has been enhanced with the subtle fragrance of red berries and precious spices. A sensual tea.

T953   THÉ DES LÉGENDES

A renaissance of age-old fragrances. Inspired by the legendary aroma of Earl Grey, this fabulous blend is composed of exquisite green teas and the smooth flavour of citrus fruit from exotic lands. An immortal tea.

T954   FILS DU CIEL

A 'Son of Heaven', in remembrance of tea fanciers. This heavenly green China tea is harmoniously combined with the fragrance of legendary fruits, evoking the memory of the Chinese emperors, those messengers of the gods. A tea to offer.

T955   THÉ SUR LE NIL

A whiff of adventure: this blend will take you to the ends of the world, where the thoughts of enchanted voyagers dwell. Citrus fruit from forgotten lands and refined spices wonderfully scent this fine green tea. A flight of fancy - a timeless tea.

T956   MONTAGNE DE JADE

A magic essence. Jade, an emblem of perfection and purity, symbolises the harmony between heaven and earth. A jade-coloured green tea has been gracefully blended with the mysterious fragrances of the famous 'Montagne d'Or' tea. A silken elixir, a potion of peace.

T957   THÉ VERT MARCO POLO

To celebrate the Year 2000, MARIAGE FRÈRES added a new chapter to its long saga of creating special blends. A green tea was carefully chosen for its smooth, natural flavour, then wed to secret fragrances of fruit and flowers from China and Tibet, as already made famous by the 'Marco Polo' blend. A tea typical of French connoisseurship.

T958   FESTIN D'OR

Created in the spirit of Oriental magnificence, this 'Golden Feast' features a blend of green tea with marigolds and Moroccan mint. The heady fragrance of fresh mint and floral scents evoke the sumptuous feasts of A Thousand and One Nights. To be enjoyed hot or cold - the pleasure of a lost paradise.

T959   BOUDDHA BLEU

For centuries, Buddhists in the Land of Free Men have perpetuated the custom of making special offerings of flowers, fruit and tea to monks. From this green tea, sprinkled with blue cornflowers, there rises a blend of fragrances recalling the ripe fruit on a tray laden with offerings. A tea steeped in spirituality.

T960 BEL AMI
'Fairest Friend' is a tribute to friendship, love and beauty.
This sensual green tea evokes warm memories of late 19th-century Paris as described in the stories of Guy de Maupassant.
Nowadays, that timeless Paris of elegant, pleasure-seeking romantics is symbolised by this tea with its scent of fresh flowers and vanilla.
For the aesthetes in this world.

T961 ALEXANDRA DAVID-NÉEL
As a tribute to the famous female explorer, MARIAGE FRÈRES has developed a blend in which black tea evokes China and the tea route, while spices such as pepper, clove, ginger, cinnamon and cardamom recall David-Néel's quest for the Orient. Meanwhile, the addition of a fresh, floral note evokes the plenitude of meditation.

T962 THÉ DES IMPRESSIONISTES
In the wild, rocky, maritime region of Provence in southern France, nature's shimmering colours create rare and intense harmonies that delighted Impressionist artists.
This green tea, scented with mild spices and white flowers, is also dotted with mauve flowers as a visual echo of the dazzling and powerful fragrance that fills the mouth.
A colourful tea.

Henri Mariage in his Tea House, Paris, 1910.

MARIAGE FRÈRES : THE TEA MUSEUM

An homage to the Majesty of Tea

ICHARD A. BUENO, HEIR TO VOYAGERS WHO PLIED THE SEAS AND CROSSED continents in order to bring back the most exclusive teas and precious objects, founded the MARIAGE FRÈRES TEA MUSEUM, which opened on the occasion of the firm's 137th anniversary. Since that time, the collection has been augmented and enhanced.

The museum is MARIAGE FRÈRES' pride and joy, for it recreates the poetic, fragrant past of the spiritual beverage by displaying some exceedingly rare objects from the history of tea.

These items include painted oak blending casks and tea chests of beech with enchanting lacquered decoration (showing a phoenix, scenes from the Peking opera, landscapes of the Yellow Mountain). Then there are tea caddies–once a luxurious, refined item–in precious lacquers and woods (rosewood, ebony), silver, copper, pewter, and ivory. The collection also features secret herbal boxes, tea pots in the most amazing shapes and materials (porcelain, terracotta, cast iron), wicker and leather travel kits for tea, sample cases used by travelling merchants and, to underscore the elegance of the museum, Chinese furnishings in carved and lacquered wood. These masterpieces are complemented by old archives documenting distant trade across the seas, confirming the beauty and nobility of the realm of tea.

Certain historical items have now been reproduced, and are on sale at the colonial counter.

MARIAGE FRÈRES invite you to share our passion by taking a trip through an emotion-filled, nostalgia-packed world that incarnates one of the fine arts of living–the art of tea connoisseurship.

The French Art of Tea

THE FRENCH ART OF TEA

Mariage Frères: The French Tea House

THE CIVILIZATION OF TEA

THE ADVENTURE OF TEA

TEA AND THE ART OF FINE LIVING

THE ART OF MAKING FINE TEA

THE ART OF STORING TEA

THE BOOK OF TEA

CLASSIFYING TEAS

THE FINEST HARVESTS

GRAND TRADITION

FLAVOURED TEAS

Mariage Frères: The Tea Museum

INDEX ©MARIAGE FRÈRES